HUNTER'S SNARE

Samantha found herself becoming dangerously attracted to the arrogant and imperious Simon Radnor even though she knew he was only interested in having a brief affair. Could she avoid being tempted into the hunter's snare?

HUNTER'S SNARE

BY
EMILY RUTH EDWARDS

MILLS & BOON LIMITED
15–16 BROOK'S MEWS
LONDON W1A 1DR

*First published in Great Britain 1986
by Mills & Boon Limited*

© Emily Ruth Edwards 1986

*Australian copyright 1986
Philippine copyright 1986
This edition 1986*

ISBN 0 263 75352 2

*Set in Monophoto Plantin 11 on 11½ pt.
01-0586 – 47255*

*Printed and bound in Great Britain by
Collins, Glasgow*

To my mother and father,
who made this venture possible,
in more ways than one.

CHAPTER ONE

SHIFTING patterns of light and shadow danced over the small red car stopped on the winding road, as the breeze off Long Island Sound wove through the branches of the trees crowding the edges of the asphalt and set the leaves to flirting with the sunshine. In the occasional gaps between the trees, the sky showed a clear, sun-lightened blue, marked by a few small, puffy clouds drifting calmly above the breeze.

A perfect summer afternoon in western Connecticut seems designed to produce happy dispositions and cheerful smiles. The driver of the car, however, was standing beside it surveying her surroundings with a scowl. A close observer, had there been one, might have noticed that the car had an odd list, easily traceable to the back left tyre, which had apparently come out the worse from an encounter with a sharp object.

Samantha Abbott—'Sam' to everyone who knew her—turned her scowl from the countryside to the cause of her displeasure. The immediate area was clearly empty of helpful inhabitants, and unless another car came along any time soon, she was on her own. Of course she knew in theory how to change a tyre, but although she normally had no quarrel with the way her slight weight was distributed over her five feet two inches, at the moment she could have wished for a bit more muscle and fewer curves.

'After all the devoted care I've given you, the least you could have done was to choose a nail closer to town to run over!' Sam informed her faithful companion. The offending tyre produced an apologetic hiss and settled down a fraction further on to the road. A reluctant grin brightened her wide green eyes and brought the dimples in her cheeks out of hiding.

'All right, I suppose I'll forgive you,' she allowed, and then grinned more broadly as she considered the probable reaction if anyone had overhead her conversing with her car.

Feeling more cheerful, she pulled forward the driver's seat and leaned into the back to find the package of emergency flares, which had worked its way under the front seat. She had been forced to stop too close for comfort to the last bend, especially considering the road had only a two-foot shoulder; and the first order of business was to set out the flares to warn anyone coming along behind her. After a moment she re-emerged with the package in hand, brushed back the short blonde curls which had fallen around her face, and headed back around the bend.

When she returned, Sam opened the hatchback and raised the cover of the compartment housing the spare tyre. As she started to unfasten the spare, she heard the sound of a car approaching from behind. Perhaps deliverance was at hand! Brightening at the thought, Sam straightened too abruptly and cracked her head smartly on the edge of the roof. Holding her sore head and muttering under her breath, she swung around— and then leapt for the side of the road, injury forgotten, as a silver Porsche swept around the bend and seemed to charge down upon her.

When the newcomer braked to a smooth halt several feet in front of her, Sam's fright-widened eyes narrowed in recognition and a surge of indignation. Hadn't the idiot seen her flares? Put some people in a fancy car, and they think they own the road! she thought righteously, easily ignoring the possibility that she had panicked unnecessarily. And why, of all people, did Simon Radnor have to be the one to come along at this moment?

Arms folded and dimples well hidden, she watched him emerge from the Porsche. A shade under six feet in height, he had a broad frame that gave an impression of massive strength, even in his beautifully tailored dark blue suit. Thick brown hair with a slight curl framed a darkly tanned face with an imperious Roman nose, firmly held mouth and a square, determined jaw. His features were too strongly marked and aggressively masculine for conventional handsomeness, but nothing in his looks explained why a maiden in distress should regard him with an unwelcoming glare. Sam, however, had reacted like a cat with its fur rubbed the wrong way the first time she had met him a couple of months ago. She didn't like his air of mocking amusement, the cynicism that was so often reflected in his hazel eyes, or the abrupt manner that turned even a request into an order. But most of all she didn't like the threatening feeling of uncertainty that he aroused in her.

As he walked towards her now, she noticed that his gaze was focused several inches below her face and suddenly realised that crossing her arms had caused the halter top she was wearing to gape alarmingly. The scathing comment on his driving habits which she was about to deliver was forgotten as she hastily dropped her arms and fought to control a blush.

'Those prim little outfits you wear in Bohlen's office don't do you justice,' he commented in greeting, a note of amusement in his rough, low voice. His eyes make a quick survey of the long, tanned legs revealed by her shorts, before rising to her flushed cheeks.

'They are not prim, they're businesslike!' Sam retorted, anger rescuing her from embarrassment as she defended the demure skirt and blouse combinations which she wore as secretary and receptionist in a doctor's office.

He just shrugged and turned to look down at the flat tyre. 'I'll get that changed for you,' he stated in his usual autocratic manner as he started to remove his jacket.

Sam felt a strong urge to tell him that she could do very nicely without his help, thank you! On the other hand, if he wanted to get hot and dirty changing her tyre, who was she to stop him? she decided, a smile beginning to curve her lips.

She looked up to meet gleaming hazel eyes which seemed to read her thoughts. 'You'll never make a poker player,' he murmured, confirming her suspicions. 'Now, take my coat and go sit down in the shade. You look a little flushed.'

Sam snatched the coat from his outstretched hand without a word and stalked over to sit on the low stone wall which ran along the road behind the trees. It was a good thing that the tyre iron was still fastened in place, she thought broodingly. A blunt instrument might have been too much of a temptation. Who did he think he was, ordering her around like a child? She had been about to offer to set out some flares up ahead, but now she was inclined to think that it would serve him right if somebody did come along and run into him. Besides, if there was a collision, the only damage would probably be to the car that hit him.

The vision of the front end of a car crumpling up like aluminium foil, while Simon Radnor stood firm and unflinching under the impact, lightened her mood. She smoothed out the wrinkles put in his jacket by her careless grip and folded it neatly over her arm.

As she watched him effortlessly removing the flat tyre, Sam idly wondered if he had any Norman ancestors. 'Radnor' was a Welsh name, but she had just finished a book about medieval England which had devoted a chapter to the powerful and ruthless Marcher lords. These Norman barons held lands on the border of England and Wales, then called the Welsh Marches, and were charged with keeping the wild Welsh tribesmen from raiding into England. They were hard, brutal, ambitious men who made their own laws, and even the king usually left them alone, as long as they kept the Welsh within bounds. Women, of course, were considered legitimate prey by such men, and many Welsh could claim descent from a Marcher lord accustomed to taking what he pleased.

Sam stared with unconscious fascination at the play of heavy muscles in Simon Radnor's back and shoulders as he worked on her car. Then she suddenly shivered and pulled her eyes away. He might be smoothed down and restrained by civilisation, but she could easily see him as a throwback to some harsh Norman lord. Closing her eyes, she began to picture how he would look in chain mail or a suit of armour.

'Ms Abbott!'

Sam looked up, startled out of her musings by the peremptory tone. She had a feeling that Simon Radnor had spoken to her before, without getting a response.

'Much as I hate to disturb your no doubt youthfully innocent daydreams,' he went on in a hatefully mocking voice, 'I've changed the tyre, and I could use a rag to wipe my hands if you have one.'

'I think there's one in the front of the car,' she returned coldly, walking by him with her nose in the air. Failing the tyre iron, dignified coolness was her best weapon if he was going to be so provocative. A woman had her own methods of dealing with uncivilised throwbacks.

She fished a piece of stained, but clean, towelling out from under the front seat. Simon Radnor accepted it with a thoughtful expression and what looked suspiciously like a glint of amusement in his eyes. He wiped his hands in silence, however, then put out one hand in a wordless demand for his jacket. Sam, who had begun to fidget under his silent regard, quickly handed it over and opened her mouth to begin a stiffly polite little speech of thanks.

But the speech turned into a startled gasp as he tossed his jacket on to the roof of her car and pulled her firmly into his arms. He cut off the beginnings of an incoherent protest by covering her parted lips with his own hard mouth in a kiss that threatened to steal her breath away.

Naturally she resisted, but she wasn't altogether sure that he even noticed. He wasn't hurting her, just holding her closely, and inescapably, against him while he explored her mouth briefly but thoroughly. Thank heavens he wasn't really wearing armour, she thought vaguely, or she'd be bruised from head to toe!

A moment later he straightened, and his hands moved to clasp her upper arms, supporting her as he stepped back. Sam needed the support as she swayed slightly, gasping for breath and staring up at him from bemused eyes.

'Just so there's no misunderstanding, that kiss wasn't payment for changing your tyre,' he stated, his hazel eyes glowing with flecks of gold. 'It was to let you know that I'm taking up the challenge you've been issuing since the first time we met.'

By the time he finished speaking, Sam's spine had straightened, and she jerked free of his loosened hold. 'You're crazy! I haven't issued any challenge to you . . . and don't you ever do that again!' she ended furiously.

His mouth quirked up. 'You look like a little blonde cat, hissing and spitting at me,' he told her. 'And you're challenging me every time you look at me with those green cat's eyes of yours, or walk by me with that patrician little nose stuck up in the air. Sooner or later,' he continued, ignoring her attempts to interrupt, 'I'm going to enjoy stroking down that ruffled fur for you.'

'You . . . you . . .!' Unable to summon up words strong enough to do justice to her feelings,

Sam marched off and climbed into her car, slamming the door behind her with a satisfying bang. Dearly as she would have liked to slap the amusement from his arrogant face, she had no reason to believe that he would take the well-deserved reproof like a gentleman—in other words, that he wouldn't retaliate—and her dignity was already in rags and tatters.

Instead she gunned the engine, popped the clutch, and took off in a cloud of dust and a great screeching of tyres. To her immense satisfaction, when she looked in her rear view mirror Simon Radnor was waving a hand in front of his face and coughing.

A few minutes later she pulled into the driveway of her home in the village of Westfield. As she walked towards the back door, which led into her kitchen, she looked with pleasure at the old two-storey frame house that had been her home for twenty-four years. Six years ago, her life had been shattered with shocking abruptness when a tractor-trailer had jack-knifed into the family car, killing her parents and leaving Sam unharmed, but trapped for three hours before rescuers could free her from the wreckage. When her lawyer-trustee had proposed selling her home to finance a college education, Sam had resisted with such fierceness that he had finally allowed her to have her way, only insisting that the second floor be converted into an apartment to provide funds for maintenance.

With her parents gone and no close relatives, Sam had clung to her family home as the only security in a suddenly threatening world. A sheltered and much-loved only child, she had been unusually close to her parents, and their loss, plus the trauma of the accident, had bitten deep. Though time had eased the pain, and she appeared to return to normal, Sam had been left with a deep need for security and safety which made her resent change and avoid taking risks. She felt none of the normal adventurous curiosity about the larger world and was content to remain quietly in Westfield, happily engrossed in familiar activities.

Making a mental note that the flower beds needed weeding again, Sam unlocked the back door and walked through to what had been the dining-room and was now an unmistakably feminine bedroom, done in off-white and green with accents of rose. As she stood under the shower a few minutes later, she went over her run-in with Simon Radnor. She had banished him from her mind on the way home after nearly missing a curve while dwelling on the lovely idea of somehow forcing him to humbly beg her forgiveness for his boorish behaviour.

That idea was still attractive, she thought wistfully as she worked up a lather of shampoo in her hair, but unfortunately she couldn't come up with a workable method of achieving this worthy goal. Thumbscrews and racks were in short supply in Westfield, though possibly they would come back into fashion, now that the village had acquired a marauding Norman baron masquerading as a businessman.

'Baron Radnor,' she said out loud, testing the sound of it. Yes, it fitted him very well. He would look right at home riding around the countryside dressed up in an armoured suit, trampling all over anyone who got in his way. If this afternoon was any example, his attitude towards women was appropriate, too, she thought darkly. Some people in Westfield might approve of him, including a surprising number of misguided females, but he hadn't fooled Sam Abbott!

She still had a vivid memory of the first time she had met him, when he had brought his grandmother, who had a heart condition, into the doctor's office where Sam worked shortly after they had moved into the old McDaniels estate. Of course, she had heard about him before then. Simon Radnor had been big news in the village ever since the announcement that he was moving the headquarters of his company, Radnor Computer Technologies, from New York to Westfield. The village gossips had been working overtime, especially after it was discovered that he was thirty-five and unmarried. Sam knew that he had no close relatives except his grandmother, that he had started Radcom on a small loan and built it into a leader in the field, and—of paramount interest to the gossips—that he showed an appreciation of beautiful women, but no inclination to settle down. Presumably his grandmother was living with him to oversee the household and play hostess in the absence of a wife.

Sam had taken a dim view of Radcom moving to the village. Where one company came, others generally followed, and then what would happen to her beloved Westfield? Industrial parks, housing developments, shopping centres— changes of all sorts, that's what would happen! Unfortunately, a majority of her neighbours were more concerned with the taxes Radcom would pay than with the evils that would follow in its train.

To say that Sam had already decided to dislike the man responsible for Radcom's coming before she met him would be an exaggeration; to say that she was ready to give him enough rope to hang himself would not. And shortly after he ushered his grandmother into the office, she was busily increasing the slack. To her critical gaze his hard-featured face positively oozed arrogance, and his eyes swept over her in a glance that seemed to categorise her and dismiss her along with the rest of the waiting-room furniture. Here was a man who would upset people's peaceful lives and merely shrug—if he ever noticed, Sam thought resentfully as he approached her desk.

Forcing a bright smile on her face, she enquired, 'May I help you . . . sir?' The pause at the end had been more intention than fact, but even his worst enemy—Sam Abbott, for instance—couldn't deny that Simon Radnor was quick.

With a slightly raised eyebrow and a sharp, enquiring glance, he replied, 'My grandmother, Helen Radnor, has a two o'clock appointment with Dr Bohlen. Are we likely to have to wait long, Miss . . .?'

Before Sam could reply, Anne Jenkins, the office nurse, poked her head into the waiting-room. 'Sam, Doctor will be ready for Mr Janowski in just a minute.'

Sam nodded and turned back to find Simon Radnor regarding her with quizzical amusement. ' "Sam"?' he questioned, his mouth quirking up to join his eyebrow as he resurveyed the half of her showing above her desk.

Part of the area he had just reviewed swelled visibly. 'Ms Abbott,' she supplied through the smile plastered on her face, ignoring his questioning of her nickname. Normally she did not mind explaining that 'Sam' was short for 'Samantha', a name she had always thought too flowery; but Simon Radnor was getting nothing from her but the basic civility demanded by her job.

'Doctor Bohlen just has one more patient before Mrs Radnor, so we shouldn't be keeping her waiting too long. In the meantime we'll need to have these forms filled in,' she said, handing him a clipboard with the new-patient forms attached.

He accepted the clipboard with a nod. 'Tell Dr Bohlen that I'll want to talk to him after he's seen my grandmother.' He turned away without waiting for an answer, then abruptly turned back again. 'Just as a matter of curiosity, *Ms* Abbott, is it me you don't like, or the fact that my company has moved into your quiet little village?'

As a child Sam's impulsiveness had been the despair of her parents. After the accident that trait had all but disappeared, but now it chose to make one of its rare appearances. 'Why, whatever do you mean, Mr Radnor?' she cooed, widening her eyes and looking the picture of overdone bewildered innocence.

There was a moment of silence.

'All right, Green Eyes, we'll leave it for now,' he said, with a slow smile which left her feeling distinctly uneasy as she watched him walk away.

Yes, that was where she had made her mistake, Sam thought now as she stepped from the shower and reached for a towel. If she had just admitted that she didn't like his wretched company moving to Westfield, he probably would have relegated her back to the ranks of the office furniture. As it was, she had aroused his curiosity and now, apparently, other interests, as well. It was bad enough feeling like a specimen under a microscope on those occasions when he accompanied his grandmother to the bi-weekly check-ups for her heart condition; after this afternoon she had the uneasy feeling she was going to look back on those days with yearning nostalgia.

Going into the kitchen, she fixed herself a glass of iced tea and sat down at the small oak table where she ate her meals. As she sipped her drink, Sam stared unseeing out the window. Maybe Simon Radnor's threat had only been made to pay her back for what he no doubt saw as her lack of proper respect. That kiss had been serious enough, she admitted, unconsciously raising her hand to touch her lips, which seemed to tingle slightly at the memory; but even Simon Radnor could hardly expect to start an affair without her co-operation, could he?

While Sam was dubiously considering the probable limits of the Baron's outrageousness, she failed to consider the possibility that he might try an indirect approach. Even if the idea of seduction had occurred to her, she would have unhesitatingly dismissed it. She had the conviction of the untested that the effects of passion on principles and self-control were overrated and was even inclined to doubt that desire born of love could be as overwhelming as novelists and poets claimed. Besides, even the thought of Simon Radnor raised her hackles, and she assumed without question that the odd sensations aroused by his kiss were attributable to anger.

In addition, affairs were by definition temporary and had no place in her plans for a secure and settled future. Some day she would marry a kind, thoughtful, dependable man. In the meantime she was content to date casually and had never questioned why none of the nice young men she agreed to go out with seemed entirely adequate for the role of her future husband.

Trying to figure out what Simon Radnor might do was pointless, Sam decided finally as she drained her glass. The worst he could do was make a nuisance of himself, and as far as she was concerned, he was already a nuisance.

About to get up to refill her glass, she heard a knock on her front door and walked down the hall to answer it. A Valkyrie in a psychedelic caftan stood in the foyer, cradling a bread basket in one arm and wearing a Cheshire Cat grin.

'Hello, Kate,' she calmly greeted this apparition. Kate Townsend was her first, and only, tenant and her closest friend. She was an art teacher at the high school and was still happily single at twenty-eight.

'I'm here to break calories with you,' Kate announced. 'This humble basket contains Kate's Special Deluxe Cinnamon Applesauce Bran Muffins.'

'You and the muffins are both welcome,' Sam grinned. 'Come on back to the kitchen. I've got iced tea in the refrigerator.'

A visit from Kate would make the world look brighter, she thought, already feeling more cheerful as she led the way down the hall. If Kate could bottle her energy and zest for life, she would drive tranquillisers and tonics off pharmacy shelves in no time.

While Sam fixed two glasses of iced tea, Kate settled her generously endowed five feet ten inches into a chair at the kitchen table, propped her feet on another, and gazed with satisfaction at trellis-patterned wallpaper, stained oak cabinets, and simulated brick flooring. 'This is the epitome of kitchens,' she stated. 'Cheerful and homey without clutter. In fact, you've done an excellent job on the whole apartment. The living-room has a touch of elegance, not to mention all those gorgeous family antiques, and the bedroom has a suspicion of decadent luxury—what more could anyone want? You should give up working for Richard and take up interior decorating. You could start on my place right away in your spare time.'

Sam, who had been laughing at Kate's description of her decor, made a face. 'What spare time? Today was my first day off in ten days.'

'Have I missed something? Like a major epidemic in Westfield?'

'No, we just lost Anne, our office nurse,' Sam explained as she joined Kate at the table. 'She got a better offer from an old flame who showed up and swept her off her feet, and we've been going crazy trying to manage without her.'

'I *am* behind on the news! But can't you get someone in temporarily until you find a permanent replacement?'

'We tried, but no luck. Richard is in New York today interviewing, though, so maybe we'll have someone permanent soon.'

'How is the Adonis of the medical world?' enquired Kate, toying with one of her long, dark blonde braids.

'Overworked. And why do I always get the feeling that you don't appreciate Richard's finer qualities?'

'I do appreciate him. A woman would have to be more than half dead not to appreciate six feet of male perfection,' Kate objected. 'The ancient Greek sculptors would have wept with joy at the sight of him.'

Sam had to laugh, but shook her head reprovingly. 'He's also an excellent doctor, a thoughtful employer, and a kind and amusing friend.' Actually, Richard Bohlen had all the qualities that any sensible woman would want in a husband, and recently she had begun to give this fact careful consideration. After all, they were good friends and had worked together in harmony for two years. Why shouldn't a closer, and permanent, relationship work just as well?

'You're down on him because he was too trusting and sincere to see through Amanda Marlowe,' Sam accused with a frown.

'I just think that he could have done more than go around looking pale and noble after she'd led him around by the nose for months and then dropped him flat for a filthy rich old geezer thirty-five years older than she is.'

'Richard looks noble all the time; he can't help that,' objected Sam. 'Besides, what did you expect him to do? Challenge the "old geezer" to a duel?'

Kate laughed and then shrugged. 'I suppose not. And I'm really quite fond of Richard, you know. It's just that I have a personal preference for men with a bit of John Wayne swagger—even if I would fight to the death rather than return to the thrilling days of yesteryear, when men were men and women took it in the neck.'

'Even John Wayne himself would need all his swagger to hold his own with you,' Sam told her affectionately.

Kate tried to look modest and failed miserably. 'True,' she admitted, 'and one day I'm going to get you to admit that you need more of a challenge than those mild-mannered, passionless types you consort with.'

'Not me! I'm quite happy as I am. But it's too bad you couldn't have changed places with me about an hour ago. You would have appreciated the situation more than I did.'

'Tell!' ordered Kate, settling back more comfortably.

By the time Sam had finished relating the afternoon's events, along with her thoughts on Simon Radnor's spiritual, if not physical, ancestors, Kate was chortling with glee.

'Just what you need . . . a little excitement to liven you up,' she approved. 'Shall I lend you my helmet and spear?'

'You're the one who likes excitement, have a go at him yourself,' Sam grumbled, then started to smile. 'I can see the headline now: "Baron Pursued by Armed Valkyrie Through Streets of Westfield!"'

'Oh, lovely,' sighed Kate when the laughter had died down. 'I really must get John to introduce me to Simon Radnor.'

John Wolinski was the latest man in Kate's life and certainly made a good physical match for her, standing six feet five inches in his stockinged feet, with broad shoulders and an impressive set of muscles. He, like Kate, was twenty-eight and had light brown hair that tended to fall over his rather low forehead, dark brown eyes, and a lopsided smile. People meeting him for the first time often assumed that his muscles were stronger than his brains, but in fact, John had a degree in electrical engineering and a Ph.D. in computer science.

'Of course, John works for Radcom now,' Sam remembered. 'Has he ever said anything about Radnor?'

'John is enthusiastic about him. But John would be enthusiastic about Vlad the Impaler, if Vlad were an expert on integrated circuits.'

Sam laughed. 'That's what I like about men— they don't get distracted by inessential details.'

At that point the phone began to ring, and Kate, who was nearest, picked up the receiver and handed it across the table.

'Hello? You're back in good time. Did you have any luck?' Sam enquired, then mouthed 'Richard' at Kate. 'No, I'm free tonight. What's up? All right, I'll see you about eight, then.' She handed the receiver back to Kate, looking puzzled.

'Don't tell me you're starting with Richard now,' Kate said disapprovingly.

'The woman Richard marries will be very

lucky,' Sam insisted, her cheeks slightly flushed. 'But he hasn't asked me out. He just said he had to see me about something important.'

'Hmmm. Maybe a bit of gossip I picked up today had a smidgen of truth in it for a change,' Kate said thoughtfully. 'The word is that Amanda is on her way back to the loving arms of her parents with a divorce decree in her pocket. Opinion seems to be divided as to whether she was tossed out by her husband with nary a jewel to her name, or is returning triumphant with a large chunk of his loot.'

'Oh, dear! I know you don't think much of him for it, but Richard did fall hard for Amanda, and he was just beginning to really get over it,' Sam said worriedly. 'I wonder if he could have heard that rumour? But why would he want to talk to me, even so?'

'Maybe he wants his hand held,' Kate suggested blandly.

'Eat your muffin!' retorted Sam.

In the event, Kate wasn't so far off.

'You want to pretend we're engaged?' Sam repeated carefully, as she stared across the small cocktail table at Richard's handsome, worried face. 'Richard, how many drinks did you have before you picked me up?'

'Shh!' cautioned Richard, glancing around the dimly lit lounge of the Westfield Pub. 'Let me explain, Sam. I've got myself in a real fix, and I'm going to end up looking like a complete fool if you won't help.'

'All right, I'll listen,' she agreed doubtfully. And she dutifully remained silent as he explained how after he had hired a new nurse, he had caught a commuter train to Connecticut—and found himself travelling with Amanda Marlowe.

'She's got a divorce, Sam. And . . . well, maybe I'm mistaken, but I got the feeling that she's ready to take up where we left off when she met that Thompson character.' Richard stopped studying his glass and looked up at Sam with an expression of anguish in his eyes. 'I still love her, Sam, but I couldn't bear to get involved again and then lose her a second time if someone better comes along.'

'Richer, you mean,' she amended absently. So much for her own tentative ideas, she thought with a mental shrug and some rueful regret.

He shook his head. 'It's not as simple as that,' he insisted. 'Amanda isn't as heartless as you make her sound.' Sam looked sceptical, but kept her doubts to herself. After a moment he continued, 'At any rate, I guess I panicked because, in spite of everything, I'm not sure I could resist her if she really is interested.'

He looked back down at his glass, which he was turning around between his long fingers. 'That's where you come in. You see, I told her that we're practically engaged.'

'Richard, for heaven's sake! The whole village knows that we've never even dated. Whatever possessed you to tell a story like that?'

He grinned ruefully, looking much younger than his thirty-two years. 'I told you—I panicked. And no one will question it. Most of Westfield has been expecting something like this for ages.'

Sam spared a moment to be thankful that he

didn't know she had begun to consider the idea herself, before observing lightly, 'You mean they expected me to catch you on the rebound after Amanda got married.'

'No, I mean that they expected me to come to my senses and realise what a sterling opportunity I've been ignoring since I took over the practice two years ago,' he corrected with a smile that drew an audible sigh from a matron two tables away.

Sam studied his beautifully cut features, azure-blue eyes, and thick blond hair, which fell naturally into sculptured locks. She couldn't blame the matron; Richard was enough to warm the cockles of any woman's heart. Strange that her affection for him had never warmed into something stronger.

'Sam?' Richard was regarding her hopefully. 'It wouldn't be an official engagement, so we could always end the arrangement at any time without a lot of fuss.'

'Ha! You should know Westfield by now. They'd be wondering where we'll have the wedding reception after we're seen together twice . . .'

Her voice trailed off as a new thought occurred to her. If word got around, sooner or later Simon Radnor would hear, too; and if his comment about stroking her fur had been serious, and not just an attempt to frighten her, then maybe Richard's crazy idea could save her some annoyance.

But the careful, sensible approach to life of the past six years wasn't to be overcome that easily. 'I don't know,' she said doubtfully. Her frowning gaze wandered around the room, only to change to one of shocked dismay at the sight of Amanda Marlowe and Simon Radnor standing in the doorway of the bar.

Had they somehow been summoned up, like demons from the deep, by her thoughts?

CHAPTER TWO

MAGICAL or not, their unexpected appearance jolted Sam into another display of imprudent impulse. 'I'll do it,' she announced abruptly, only to be immediately stricken with a mixture of apprehensive doubt and a strange exhilaration.

Richard smiled in relief and reached for her hand. 'Thank you, Sam.' He raised his glass, still innocently unaware of the enemy's approach. 'How about a toast to seal the agreement?'

Perfect! thought Sam, shaking off doubt for the moment. A charming romantic scene which certain persons were unlikely to miss. She smiled sweetly and touched her glass to Richard's, then thoughtfully waited until after he had swallowed to whisper, 'Don't let go of my hand—Amanda just came in with Simon Radnor, and they're headed this way.'

Richard stiffened and his grip on her hand tightened painfully, but to her admiration, he appeared no more than pleasantly surprised by the unexpected encounter when the newcomers arrived at their table.

'Hello again, darling,' Amanda cooed at him, giving him the full benefit of big blue eyes. 'And dear Samantha, too!' she added with a distinctly edged smile.

Sam was amused. Amanda had used her full name on purpose, knowing perfectly well that she didn't like it. In fact, many years ago she had pushed Amanda into a large mud puddle just to emphasise that point! And she would be happy to do it again, she decided as she caught the hungry look in Richard's eyes.

Not that she could blame him, Sam admitted fairly. Even she could not deny that Amanda was beautiful, with her perfect features and unusual red-gold hair. And tonight, her slender figure was displayed—or over-displayed, depending upon your point of view—in a silky blue dress with no excess material above the waistline.

Suddenly Sam stiffened as a hand came to rest against the back of her chair and, seemingly by accident, brushed against her bare shoulders, left uncovered by the halter neck of her dress.

'Samantha . . . Bohlen,' Simon Radnor's rough voice greeted briefly as Sam leaned forward slightly and tried to repress the shiver that ran down her spine. Revulsion, she assured herself.

'Look, how silly to sit at two tables when we all know each other,' Amanda way saying with a silvery laugh that sounded tinny to Sam.

'Of course, please join us,' Richard replied smoothly, 'though we won't be here long. I promised to take Sam to Janson's in a little while. We haven't been dancing for some time.

Well done! Sam applauded silently as Richard seated Amanda and then moved off with Simon Radnor to find extra chairs and get more drinks from the bar.

'I must admit I was more than a bit surprised to hear that you and Richard are thinking of getting engaged,' Amanda remarked sweetly. 'I know he always looked on you as a younger sister.'

'Things have changed while you've been away,'

Sam answered cheerfully, girding herself mentally for battle.

'But I'm back now, and I'm looking forward to renewing old . . . friendships,' came the reply, a touch of steel in the tone.

'And starting new ones?' Sam enquired, turning her eyes deliberately towards Simon Radnor. As she did so, she suddenly wondered what Amanda and Radnor were doing here together. When and where had they met?

Before Amanda could answer Sam's pointed question and possibly throw some light on the subject, the men returned. 'Here you are, darlings! Samantha and I have just been getting caught up.'

Richard smiled weakly and gave Sam an anxious look as he handed her a fresh drink. Simon, she noted, gave Amanda a look of cynical disbelief, which spoke well of his intelligence, but left her even more curious about why he was escorting her.

Apparently the same question had occurred to Richard. 'Have you two known each other long?' he asked, looking from one to the other.

'Actually, we just met,' Amanda confided. 'Daddy's law firm is handling a legal matter for Simon, and he stopped by with some papers just before Daddy and Mummy left for a party. There I was, about to be left all alone on my first night home, so Simon took pity on me.'

Sam was pleased to have the matter cleared up—the Baron had been outmanoeuvred by one or more Marlowes—but Richard's relief was so obvious that she was tempted to kick him under the table.

'I suppose you two are celebrating finding a new nurse for the office,' Amanda continued. 'Richard was telling me how hard you've been working, Samantha. And I must say you do look a bit worn down.'

'I'm cultivating the ethereal look,' Sam answered promptly. 'And we are celebrating— partly because of finding a new nurse, and partly because Richard isn't on call, so we'll have a whole evening without interruptions.'

Richard was looking anxious again and hastily interposed to ask after Amanda's parents. A few minutes later he looked at his watch. 'Well, this has been pleasant . . .' For whom? Sam wondered '. . . but I promised Sam dancing tonight, and we'd better be going.'

'Simon, why don't we join them?' Amanda put in quickly. 'It's too early to go home yet, and I haven't been dancing in ages.'

Simon shrugged. 'Perhaps Richard and Samantha would rather be alone,' he suggested smoothly.

Richard and Sam exchanged glances. Put that way, they could hardly agree without seeming rude; and although Sam was willing to let politeness go by the board, she could see that Richard wasn't. So she gave him a faint nod and mentally cursed Simon Radnor. She was certain that he had done that on purpose and wished she knew exactly what he was up to, besides no good.

On their way to Janson's, which was a couple of miles north of Westfield, Richard apologised to Sam. 'I hadn't intended this evening to be our first major appearance,' he added ruefully.

Separated from their audience, Sam was falling

prey to an attack of second thoughts, but she couldn't bring herself to voice them when Richard was so clearly grateful for her help. Instead she shrugged and said with determined cheerfulness, 'Since the performance is for Amanda's benefit, she might as well be the first audience.'

He looked relieved and then smiled. 'Maybe this isn't the best time to tell you, but I failed an acting course in college.'

'That's all right,' she told him solemnly. 'All you have to do is gaze at me adoringly. And since I'm naturally adorable, you shouldn't have any problems!'

Janson's had a good crowd, as usual, but the two couples managed to find an unoccupied booth along the back wall. Usually Sam preferred to sit at the back since the decibel level was slightly lower; but before long she decided that this time she would have welcomed a table closer to the central speakers, where conversation was all but impossible as long as music was playing. The noise might give her a headache, but listening to Amanda was likely to cause a worse one.

As soon as they were seated, Amanda had embarked on a series of reminiscences directed at Richard, with occasional explanations for Simon Radnor's benefit that all seemed to begin, 'Richard and I . . .' And though Richard did his best to include Sam in the conversation, his natural politeness, and his unwilling enjoyment of the memories, handicapped him and left him no match for Amanda.

By the time the waitress came to get their

order, Sam had changed her mind about ordering ginger ale to keep a clear head and asked for a gin and tonic instead. Since Amanda wasn't giving her a chance to play her role anyway she might as well bolster her endurance, she decided grimly. In addition, Simon was observing all three of them in a way that made Sam feel uneasy. She had a sneaking suspicion that Amanda had passed on the engagement story on the way here, which would account for the cynical amusement she detected in his expression as Amanda continued to monopolise Richard.

The ten minutes until the waitress returned convinced Sam that Einstein had missed something: you didn't have to travel at enormous speed to turn minutes into hours; Amanda had discovered a way to do that sitting still. But enough was enough, and she grabbed her chance the next time Amanda paused to draw breath.

'You promised me some dancing,' she reminded Richard.

'So I did,' he responded with commendable promptness. 'If you two will excuse us . . .'

Sam loved to dance, and Richard was a good, if conservative, partner. At first she just gave herself up to the music, releasing some of the tension that had been building up in her. After a while, though, she noticed that Richard kept glancing over towards the other side of the dance floor. Looking over to see what was attracting his attention, she spotted Amanda dancing with Simon. Simon's dark business suit stood out among the more colourful, less formal attire of the men around him, but he looked perfectly at ease, and she had to admit that he moved with an unexpected grace for a man of his build.

Just then he turned his head, and one eyebrow went up as he caught her staring. To her annoyance Sam felt herself start to blush and hurriedly looked away. Drat the man! He had a real knack for throwing her off balance, she thought resentfully, feeling tension begin to coil up inside her again.

Noticing that Richard's attention had wandered again, she hissed, 'Stop staring at Amanda!' and then felt guilty when he nodded and gave her an apologetic glance. Poor Richard had enough problems without her taking out her annoyance on him.

By the time the dance ended, Sam was glad to go back to the booth and sit down. She took a gulp of her drink and sat back with a sigh.

'Tired?' asked Richard, turning sideways to look at her.

'Just ready to sit the next one out,' she replied with a rueful smile, trying to ignore the faint throbbing which had started in her temples. 'Do you mind?'

He shook his head. 'I'll sit here and practise gazing at you adoringly while you gather your strength.' He leaned closer and assumed an idiotically lovesick expression.

'You look like a sheep with a stomach ache!' she informed him between giggles.

He laughed and gave her a hug. 'That's better,' he approved, dropping a light kiss on her forehead.

Neither of them was aware that they had an audience until Amanda suddenly spoke up, her voice pitched a bit higher than normal. 'I thought we came here to dance! You two haven't given up already, have you?'

Sam looked up quickly and caught an odd expression in Amanda's eyes. If she hadn't known better, she would have said that the girl was genuinely hurt by the affectionate scene she had interrupted. Richard didn't seem to notice anything, though.

'We haven't given up. Sam's just recouping her energy for another round,' he replied cheerfully.

'Then come dance with me,' Amanda coaxed. When he hesitated, she added, 'Simon wants to sit out for a bit, too, and he can keep Samantha company. So she won't mind, will you, Samantha?'

In a pig's eye, I won't, thought Sam. But she was afraid that if she objected, Amanda would take it as a sign that she was unsure of Richard. And since she could hardly explain that what she objected to was being left alone with Simon Radnor, Sam did her best to appear perfectly content with the arrangement.

When Richard and Amanda had left, Simon slid into the booth, which immediately shrank, and caught her eye before she could look away. 'Too bad you didn't get the good doctor securely tied down before the competition turned up, Green Eyes,' he commented, confirming her earlier suspicion that Amanda had filled him in. 'If tonight is any example, I wouldn't offer very good odds on your chances of success now.'

'Of all the nerve . . .!' Sam might not be feeling her best, but there was still some fight left in her. 'My relationship with Richard is none of your business,' she told him furiously. 'And I will never understand how a lovely person like your grandmother could be related to someone so rude!'

'Forthright, not rude, Samantha,' he corrected imperturbably, before continuing. 'And you should be grateful to Amanda. She's going to help save you from making a terrible mistake.'

'Marrying Richard would not be a mistake!'

'Oh, I'm sure he'll make a charming husband, but not for you, little cat. You have too much passion locked inside you to settle for a lover you're merely fond of.' As he spoke, his eyes moved down to her mouth.

'And you know nothing about me—or how I feel about Richard,' Sam got out through gritted teeth, struggling to control her seething outrage before she confirmed his opinon of her temperament by emptying her glass in his face. At the same time one distant part of her mind was as upset by her own reactions as by the Baron's words; this was the second time today that he had succeeded in destroying her usual calm control.

'I've seen you and Richard together,' the Baron replied with a shrug which indicated that an hour's observation would be enough for anyone to draw the obvious conclusion about her feelings. 'Besides, I do know a good bit about you from my grandmother.'

Sam felt suddenly exposed. She had taken to Mrs Radnor as quickly as she had taken against her grandson, and since Mrs Radnor came to the office every other week, they had had many opportunities to chat. The conversations had not seemed particularly intimate or revealing at the time, but now she felt uneasy.

That was silly, though, she assured herself a moment later. What difference did it make if he knew her whole life history? She had nothing to hide. Besides, knowing a collection of facts didn't mean you knew a person. Trying to banish from her mind the old dictum that knowledge is power, she refocused her gaze on Simon Radnor, who was observing her with a slight smile.

'This conversation is completely pointless,' she stated with cold dignity.

'All right, we'll change the subject for now if you find this one too difficult,' he agreed.

'I don't want to talk about anything!' she snapped back, dignity forgotten. Really, he was enough to enrage a saint! Besides, the throbbing in her temples was growing worse, and she had the horrible feeling that one of her rare migraine headaches might be coming on.

Instead of making the cutting reply which she was half expecting, Simon merely shrugged. 'Then we'll dance instead.'

Before she could object, he slid out of the booth and took her hand in a grip which suggested that she was going to be joining him whether she wanted to or not. Sam had no desire to be dragged bodily from the booth, and she had already allowed him to pull her to her feet before it dawned on her that the music had changed tempo.

'I don't want to dance, either!' she hissed, no longer compliant as he switched his grip to her elbow and started towards the dance floor.

He calmly ignored her surreptitious tugs and dragging feet. 'Don't worry,' he murmured as they reached the open space where closely entwined couples were swaying to slow, romantic music under dimmed lights. 'I know you're tired, but you can rest while we dance. Just put your arms around my neck and lean on me. I'll do the rest.'

He turned her gently to face him, his hazel eyes glowing gold with laughter. About to attempt a crushing retort, Sam found her own gaze caught by the warmth genuine amusement gave his face, and her words went unspoken. Then her eyes fell to the broad shoulder so close to her; and as if her mind had shifted focus, the strength that had seemed threatening suddenly seemed to offer irresistible comfort and support for her throbbing head.

As she slid her arms around his neck, she felt him stiffen for an instant before his arms came around to hold her firmly against him. She would probably be furious with herself tomorrow, she thought vaguely, but right now it felt so good to relax and just lean on him as he had suggested . . .

Simon Radnor stared down at the blonde head resting so trustingly against his shoulder, his dark brows knit in a thoughtful frown. Then he gave a mental shrug and shifted his arms slightly to pull Samantha even closer. She must have had more to drink than he had thought. Unless the little devil was just trying to shut him up by distracting him.

He smiled wryly and brushed his lips against a tickling curl. Holding her like this was distracting, all right! If she could read his mind right now, she would probably stalk off the dance floor with her nose in the air like an insulted Siamese. At twenty-four, she undoubtedly had some experience with men, but he was willing to bet that she had no more than a nodding acquaintance with true passion. She was apparently serious about marrying Richard Bohlen, yet he had seen no signs of any feeling stronger than affection from either of them.

Simon glanced over to where Richard and Amanda were moving slowly to the music, seemingly absorbed in each other. His grandmother, who had an uncanny knack of gathering information in spite of rarely going out, had related to him the history of Richard's relationship with Amanda. And while he suspected that Samantha was looking for a nice, safe marriage to an equivalent of the boy-next-door, he guessed that Richard was seeking an antidote for his unhappy attraction to Amanda Marlowe.

Samantha's head moved against his shoulder, interrupting his thoughts, and he slid one hand up to thread his fingers into the silky curls. He wasn't in much better case than Richard, Simon admitted wryly. He had been attracted to Samantha at their first meeting, but by now the attraction had grown into an almost obsessive desire. At first he had fought it, seeing the potential for problems. Samantha was the sort of woman who thought more in terms of marriage than affairs, and revealing his interest might give her ideas—not to mention what Gran would make of it, given his usual predilection for sophisticated, experienced women. But when he had found himself making excuses to go with his grandmother to her doctor's appointments, he had decided that the only solution was to try to satisfy the obsession and handle any problems if, and when, they arose. He wasn't, after all, a stranger to taking risks, or Radcom would never have survived and prospered.

As for this imminent engagement, he would see what developed . . .

The throbbing in Sam's head had settled into a constricting band running across her forehead and ending in a knot at the nape of her neck. One part of her mind was aware that she was definitely having a migraine and ought to get help. But finding Richard among the crowd of dancers seemed an insurmountable task in her present condition, and she was loath to leave the protection of Simon Radnor's strong arms, which were holding her so securely to the comforting shelter of his body. Then the choice was taken from her.

'Samantha?' The enclosing arms started to withdraw. 'I hate to break this up, but the music has stopped, and——' The hands which had been gently easing her away suddenly tightened. 'What's wrong, Samantha? Are you feeling sick?'

The Baron was frowning, Sam noticed as she looked up through eyes half-closed to shield abnormally dilated pupils. He probably thought she was drunk; she should tell him what was wrong. She opened her mouth to speak, only to realise that she couldn't remember the word for her illness. This side effect was always disconcerting: she would know what she wanted to say, but some part of her brain was temporarily paralysed, and the right word wouldn't come to her.

'Sweetheart, what is it?' he questioned softly when she continued to stare at him without speaking.

She gave up the attempt to remember the word 'migraine' and did her best without. 'Not drunk,' she stated in a slurred voice. 'Head hurts.' Then she added, 'Need Richard.'

But he was already moving. With one arm around her waist, he half-coaxed, half-carried her back towards the booth where the other two were now waiting.

Richard spotted them and started forward. 'What's wrong?'

'She says her head hurts,' the Baron answered grimly before she could speak.

'Richard, mi . . . mi . . .'

'Yes, I know,' Richard interrupted soothingly as he drew her into the support of his own arm. 'You have a migraine. We'll go home now and give you something for it.'

'I'll take care of the check,' the Baron said abruptly. 'Do you want Amanda's help with her?'

'Kate should be there,' Sam heard Richard reply.

'Then wait here, Amanda,' the Baron ordered. 'I'll be right back.'

Bossy man! Sam thought, before Amanda's name triggered another thought, and she pulled back as Richard started to move away. Polite to the last, she turned her head with great care towards the other woman and managed, 'Sorry. Good night.' She noticed that Amanda looked concerned, but that was probably because her own eyes were not focusing properly.

Richard said something over his shoulder as they started moving again, but Sam didn't pay any attention. Her thoughts were centred on other matters. 'Feel sick,' she commented dolefully as they left the club.

'Here, sit her down on this wall and give me your keys. I'll bring your car around.'

The sound of that rough voice, combined with the mention of a car, recalled an unfortunate memory to Sam's mind. 'No!' she refused loudly, then muttered, 'Nasty Baron.'

'Hush, Sam,' Richard ordered softly as he shifted her slightly to get at his keys. 'Simon is talking to me.'

Sam subsided obediently and, from then on, concentrated on controlling the feeling of nausea and enduring the mass of pain in her head to the exclusion of all else.

When Sam woke up Thursday morning, the first thing she was aware of was that the intolerable pressure in her head was gone. Then her feeling of relief disappeared as memories of the previous evening began to filter through. How could she have agreed to Richard's crazy scheme? It was all Radnor's fault! He was a dangerous, disruptive influence; whenever he was around, he brought out the childish impulsiveness that she thought she had left safely behind her for ever. And now she was stuck with the consequences. Even if she could bring herself to let Richard down, they would both look like fools. Besides, she might still end up being grateful for whatever protection Richard could offer her, she thought with a certain lack of consistency.

Sam buried her face in the pillow and groaned, then twisted around abruptly when she heard the rustle of covers· from the matching twin bed on her left. Head propped on hand,

Kate lay stretched out on her side, her hair spread out around her shoulders like a golden cape.

'The Sleeping Beauty finally awakes,' she commented, surveying Sam from drowsy blue eyes. 'How are you feeling?'

Sam sat up. 'The migraine is gone. But what are you doing here?'

'I'm playing angel of mercy, bringing succour to the afflicted ... buttering up my landlady,' Kate answered solemnly. 'Don't you remember my being here last night? Whoo-o did you think undressed you and put you into your nightie?'

'I hadn't got as far as worrying about that,' Sam admitted. 'And I do vaguely remember you shoving me around, before Richard gave me a shot and I zonked out.'

'That was a firm guiding hand, my child,' corrected Kate. 'At any rate, I stayed to keep an eye on you. And to tell you when you woke up that you're under doctor's orders to stay at home today and do your best imitation of a lady of leisure.'

'Thank you for staying, Kate, your landlady much appreciates the gesture,' said Sam as she threw back the sheet and got up. 'But I can't possibly stay home today. The new nurse isn't due until Monday, and Richard will end up with a migraine if he tries to cope by himself.'

'At least call him before you start dashing around,' Kate suggested.

Sam glanced at her alarm clock, which showed eight o'clock. 'All right, I'll call now. He should be at the office.'

Richard was pleased to hear that she felt fine,

but ordered her to stay home. 'Then I won't feel
so guilty,' he told her.

'Why should you feel guilty?'

'Your migraines seem to be related to tension,
and I was the one who talked you into a tense
situation. Maybe we should forget the whole
idea.'

'We can't stop now,' she said stoutly, stifling
her own lingering misgivings. 'And it was Simon
Radnor who was making me so tense, not playing
your beloved.'

'Ah, yes—the Nasty Baron!'

Sam gasped. 'Where did you come up with that
name?'

'That's what you called him last night in
Janson's parking lot,' he told her cheerfully,
confirming her worst fears. She noted a bit sourly
that Richard seemed to have recovered re-
markably fast from his pangs of guilt.

'Take that grin off your face, and tell me if he
heard,' she demanded.

'How do you know I'm——'

'Richard!'

'All right,' he laughed, 'but the truth is, I can't
tell you for sure. You only muttered it, so it
depends how good his hearing is.'

'Oh, terrific!' she moaned. 'He can probably
hear a pin drop at fifty paces.'

'I take it that "baron" comes from that
commanding air he has?' Richard questioned.

'More or less,' she answered vaguely.

'Well, I wouldn't worry about it. Simon is
really quite decent, and besides, I doubt if he's
succeeded in such a competitive field without
being called worse,' consoled Richard, still

sounding amused. 'By the way, if you still care, you won't be leaving me in the lurch today. Amanda will be here shortly to help out.'

That got Sam's attention. 'Amanda *Marlowe*?'

'I know she isn't trained or experienced, but she still can answer phones and move people in and out of the office,' he pointed out defensively. 'Amanda was very worried about you last night, Sam. She called after I got home to make sure you were all right, and she offered right away to come in to help out after I said that I would prefer you to stay home today.'

'Did she?' Sam responded neutrally. She could think of another interpretation of this noble offer of help, though her spotty recollection of the previous evening did include a memory of Amanda looking concerned.

'She has changed,' Richard insisted. 'Oh, I know she didn't behave very well last night, but there *was* a difference. The real Amanda seemed . . . closer to the surface, I guess you could say.'

In Sam's opinion the real Amanda had been on obnoxious display the previous evening, and Richard's reaction worried her. But she knew better than to argue the point when he was already feeling defensive.

'Well, tell her I appreciate the concern and her filling in today,' she said peaceably. 'But remember who you're supposed to be in love with!'

'Yes, dear.'

She wandered back into the bedroom with a smile lingering on her face. 'I'm staying home, Kate, so let's fix a sinfully fattening breakfast, and then I'll tell you about last night.'

Late afternoon found Sam in the backyard, restoring order to the flowerbeds. Kate was upstairs working on some project in her kitchen, and occasional snatches of familiar songs rendered with the Townsend touch wafted down from the open window. The calypso version of *Figaro* was the most successful, Sam decided, though she rather liked *Oh, Susannah* rescored for a Wagnerian opera.

Kate was in good form today, which no doubt proved that starting the day chortling merrily at a friend's expense was even better than starting with a smile, she thought ruefully. She should have guessed that Kate would find the whole situation a cause for amusement rather than alarm.

'You're not hurting anyone by pretending to have a serious relationship with Richard,' Kate had pointed out. 'Even if Amanda really regrets throwing Richard over and plans to keep the poor chump this time, it won't do her any harm to go through a little jealousy before she snags him. And it's about time something happened to shake you out of your rut. You've been hiding away in your safe, tidy little world for too long. If Simon Radnor can force you out of your shell, I say, more power to him.'

Kate had always disapproved of her preference for the quiet life and disinclination for taking any risks, but delivering her into the clutches of the Baron, so to speak, was rather extreme, Sam thought. Then her cheeks reddened with embarrassed annoyance as a picture formed in her mind of herself literally in the Baron's clutches last night—with her own willing co-operation, too.

What in the world could she have been thinking of to offer him that sort of encouragement? Even a migraine shouldn't have muddled her brain that much! Sam jabbed recklessly at another weed, gravely imperilling an innocent marigold growing nearby. Her behaviour made about as much sense as Little Red Riding Hood cuddling up to the wolf.

'Samantha!' barked the wolf, from directly behind her. 'What do you think you're doing?'

Sam nearly jumped out of her skin at the unexpected voice. Then she took a couple of deep breaths, stuck her trowel carefully into the ground, and got deliberately to her feet. But before she could deliver a few well-chosen words on the lack of elementary consideration shown by persons who sneaked up on other persons and scared them out of ten years' growth, Simon spoke again.

'Richard told me you're supposed to be resting today,' he growled, his brows drawn together in a frown of lordly displeasure as he surveyed the sweat-darkened tendrils of hair clinging to her temples and the streak of dirt decorating her chin.

He himself was immaculately clad in a pearl-grey, three-piece suit created by an artist of the tailoring world, and Sam, conscious of her own disreputable shorts and shirt, added all the natural annoyance of someone caught at a disadvantage to his other offences.

'It's none of your business what I do, Mr Radnor,' she informed him with an attempt at quelling haughtiness—which she might have foregone, had she been aware of her dirty chin.

'There's no need to be so formal, Samantha.

My name is Simon,' he told her, his frown now replaced by a look of amusement which didn't please her any better. But since he had brought up the subject of names, she decided to pursue another sore point.

'*My* name is Sam,' she returned pointedly.

He gave her a crooked grin, and for once his hard features showed none of the mockery which she had come to expect. Sam was appalled by the tug of attraction she felt as his dark face was transformed by an appealing charm. The migraine must have taken more out of her than she had realised.

'Nice try, sweetheart,' he applauded, 'but you can't go on calling me "Mr Radnor" without looking ridiculous, so you don't have enough bargaining power. Besides,' he continued, 'I had a beagle named Sam when I was a boy, and I find it difficult to call you by the same name when you're so different from him.'

Sam might have largely subdued her impulsiveness, but her sense of humour had remained a weak point. 'Well, I can't say I'm sorry to hear that I don't remind you of a beagle,' she found herself admitting, a grin tugging at the corners of her mouth.

'Oh, no,' he said regretfully. 'Sam was very obedient and completely devoted to me.'

'By all means call me Samantha,' she urged wryly. 'I wouldn't want to take the slightest chance of your confusing us!'

'Thank you. And now, perhaps you'll explain what you're doing grubbing around in a flowerbed when you're supposed to be taking it easy,' he suggested smoothly.

'Really, Simon,' she started to protest, 'that's——'

'Don't tell me it's none of my business,' he interrupted, his dark brows snapping together as all traces of humour disappeared from his voice. 'You gave me the worst fright I've had in a long time last night, so you can damn well allow me the right to be concerned!'

He wasn't joking, Sam realised in amazement as she searched his set expression. Well, of course she had never thought that he was totally devoid of normal human emotions—she had seen enough evidence of his affection and concern for his grandmother, for example—but in general he seemed so invulnerable that she felt disarmed by his reaction. She also became aware that they were standing in the hot sun, and that she, at least, was thirsty.

'Come inside and have something to drink,' she suggested impulsively. 'We might as well argue about my invalid status in comfort.'

He looked at her sharply, as if wondering if she were merely stalling, then his features relaxed. 'Good idea,' he nodded.

'Coke, iced tea, or something stronger?' she asked as she led the way into the kitchen.

'Coke will be fine,' he answered, reaching up to loosen the knot of his tie and undo the collar buttons of his shirt as he gazed around the bright yellow and green kitchen.

Something in his stance, combined with that very masculine action, spoke so strongly of the arrogant male surveying his domain that Sam had to fight down a moment of panic. Turning quickly to the sink to wash her hands, she scolded herself for being so ridiculous. What was she afraid of? Being dragged by the hair into the bedroom in lieu of a cave? Really, her reactions were getting more primitive than the Baron's! This was her own familiar home, and she was perfectly safe here.

'Have a seat,' she invited, glancing over her shoulder as she moved to a cabinet to get glasses.

'Who lives upstairs?' asked Simon as he started over to the table. 'Gran mentioned that you own this place and rent out the second floor,' he added before she could question how he knew about the upstairs apartment.

'Oh. Well, Kate Townsend lives there. She's the art teacher at the high school,' Sam answered as she joined him with their drinks.

'I take it that's the Kate Richard said he would get to help him with you,' commented Simon, apparently making idle conversation.

Sam nodded. 'She got me into bed and then stayed the night to keep an eye on me ... unnecessarily, I might add,' she finished with a pointed look.

He relaxed imperceptibly, having gained the information he was after. He had been surprised how strongly he had reacted to the idea of Richard undressing Samantha, even though Richard was a doctor and possibly, though he was inclined to doubt it, Samantha's lover. This obsession seemed to have awakened all his possessive instincts with a vengeance.

'I'm sure it was unnecessary,' he agreed in reply to her last remark. 'You couldn't get up to much mischief while you were asleep.'

'I am not four years old,' she informed him

indignantly. 'And I've been taking care of myself quite successfully for six years now. I hadn't been out in the garden for more than half an hour before you arrived, and after a morning spent lying around inside, I needed a little fresh air and exercise!'

'So there!' he murmured.

Sam glared at him, but couldn't hold it when she met the gleam of laughter in his eyes. 'You're impossible,' she accused, trying to hide a smile. When his lips curved in an answering smile, she felt that tug of attraction again. This time, though, instead of being appalled, she began to wonder if she had been unfairly prejudiced against him from the beginning.

'Gran would tell you that I come by it naturally,' he answered. 'According to her, all Radnor men have managing dispositions, and any sensible woman would find them infuriating.'

She laughed. 'And how does she account for the fact that she married one?'

'She claims that he took unfair advantage of a moment of weakness and then got her in front of a minister before she'd come to her senses,' Simon explained, and watched with pleasure as her green eyes were lit by laughter.

'That sounds just like her,' Sam said fondly. 'I always look forward to her visits to the office. She's such fun to talk to—if I can afford to let my work go for a few minutes,' she added hastily, a blush staining her cheekbones as she remembered belatedly that she had always avoided conversation when Simon had accompanied Mrs Radnor.

'I've noticed how busy you often are,' he commented with a sardonic look. But to her relief, the look disappeared as he went on to say, 'Gran enjoys your conversations, too. She's talked about inviting you out to the house some time, but I think she worries about imposing on you.'

'She wouldn't be imposing at all,' Sam responded instantly. 'Besides,' she went on honestly, 'I'm dying to see what you've done to the place. So is the rest of the town, I might add. The workmen you used have been drained of every last little detail.'

Simon looked amused. 'I'll have to give a party soon to satisfy all that seething curiosity.' He pushed back his chair and stood up. 'But you won't have to wait for that, or an invitation from Gran, to see what's been done.'

'Oh?' she said doubtfully, feeling wary again as he stood looking down at her, a little smile playing around his lips.

'I know we were all disappointed that our evening had to be cut short last night, so when I called your office this morning to check on you, I issued an invitation for Sunday afternoon to try out the new swimming pool. Richard said you hadn't made any plans yet, and Amanda was very enthusiastic about the idea.'

Sam opened her mouth and then shut it again without saying anything. The last thing she wanted was a repeat of that cosy foursome. And she had a good idea that the Baron was well aware of her feelings, since he had neatly timed his announcement to catch her by surprise and not give her a chance to come up with a prior engagement. And to think that she had almost been ready to decide that she had misjudged this underhanded, deceitful . . .

'Shame on you, Samantha!'

The comment was so apposite, considering the word she was about to use, that for one moment Sam wondered if she had spoken aloud.

'A lady doesn't even think in that sort of language,' he went on reprovingly, then watched with appreciation as the stricken expression which had appeared for an instant on her face was replaced by a look which, by rights, should have shrivelled him where he stood.

The Baron turned and strolled to the door. Looking back over his shoulder, he remarked, 'You have a streak of dirt on your chin,' then pushed open the door and disappeared down the steps.

CHAPTER THREE

NOT even a simple 'goodbye,' or 'thanks for the Coke,' Sam thought indignantly, rubbing furiously at her chin. Come to think of it, he hadn't said 'hello,' either. No doubt he didn't like to waste his precious time exchanging pleasantries with the peasantry! And if that abrupt manner did mask a tiny amount of charm, it was now quite clear that it also covered a sly, conniving nature—like a computer with a nasty sense of humour.

At that point a loud pounding summoned her to her front door. She opened it to find Kate, with a horned helmet on her head, a spear grasped firmly in one hand, and a sternly resolute expression knitting her brows. Even Sam's ill humour was no match for this assault, but she did manage to keep a straight face.

'I'm sorry, little girl, but you're too early for Hallowe'en.'

'I've come to protect you from the evil Baron,' Kate announced reproachfully.

'I notice you waited until the foe had left the field to rush down here,' Sam got out, before giving way to laughter. It was the T-shirt with 'Kiss Me, I'm Polish' emblazoned on the front that provided the final perfect touch to the outfit, she decided, expecially since it was obviously an old one of John's and hung down almost past Kate's shorts.

'Details, details,' said Kate grandly, waving

aside Sam's petty complaint with her spear. 'That *was* Simon Radnor I saw outside, wasn't it?'

'The one and only,' Sam confirmed. 'Come on back to the kitchen, Brünnhilde.'

When Kate had seated herself in the chair Simon had just vacated, she propped the spear against the wall and removed her helmet with a grimace. 'I havn't had this thing out since the faculty show last year. It's covered with dust!' She nodded agreement to Sam's offer of a Coke and then asked, 'So what was his lordship doing here?'

'Checking up on me. Apparently his dancing doesn't usually have such a strong effect on his partners,' Sam answered drily.

'Overwhelmed him, did you? Well, I can't say that I blame him. I remember all too clearly the first time you pulled that little trick on me,' said Kate with a shudder. 'Was the shock enough to cause him to repent his evil ways?'

Sam's first reaction was to pour scorn on the very idea, but the truth was that except for the nasty surprise he had sprung on her at the end, Simon had not seemed at all like the cold, cynical, arrogant man she had thought she knew.

'Actually,' she replied slowly, 'it's possible— just possible, mind you, that I allowed my dislike of Radcom moving here to prejudice me against him. And his abrupt manner didn't help, either.' She paused and then added thoughtfully, 'But I still don't trust him. He's too ... well, he's just "too," that's all!'

'What you mean is that he makes you feel unsettled, and that makes you feel threatened,' interpreted Kate. 'Not that I blame you for the "unsettled" part. I was feeling a bit that way myself just discreetly observing him from my second-storey window. Whatever the man lacks, it's not sex appeal.'

Sam shifted uncomfortably in her chair. 'He can be rather charming when he wants to be,' she agreed reluctantly.

'Charming!' Kate repeated in disgust. 'What has charm to do with sex appeal? Is Marlon Brando *charming*?'

Sam flushed and made haste to change the subject by telling Kate about the swimming party which Simon had sprung on her.

Kate was sympathetic, but could only suggest that Sam choose her moment and drown Amanda, thus relieving herself of at least one irritant.

On Sunday afternoon Sam put on her most conservative bikini, covered it with a sundress, and stuffed underwear, a beach robe, and various odds and ends into a carry-all. Then she sat down glumly by her living room window to watch for Richard. He had called on Thursday night and was so clearly looking forward to the outing on Sunday that she hadn't had the heart to tell him that she wished he hadn't accepted.

She had ventured one question, though: 'Won't it bother you to see Amanda with someone else?'

'It might, except Amanda didn't seem interested in the Nasty Baron, except to warn me that she thinks he has his eye on you.'

'Kind of her,' Sam had returned sourly.

It had occurred to her afterwards that she should have been disappointed, since a match-up between Amanda and Simon would solve their problems quite neatly. In fact, she did not find the idea at all appealing, though she attributed this to a concern for Richard's feelings. Better for him if Amanda left the area before she latched on to a new man.

A weather forecast for a rainy weekend had raised her spirits for a while, and a dreary, overcast Saturday sent her to bed with a happy smile. Unfortunately, thunder showers during the night cleared the skies, and Sunday morning brought sunshine and clean, clear air that fairly sparkled as a light breeze carried away the raindrops clinging to leaves and flowers.

Sam was outraged.

Mother Nature must have been laughing up her sleeve the last couple of days, she thought as she slumped in her chair glowering out at the lovely day. But even the prospect of hours with the Baron and Amanda was not enough to sustain her gloom after her eyes wandered to the family of robins in the silver maple just outside her window. She had been keeping an eye on them since Mama and Papa had set up housekeeping in the spring. Now the family numbered three, and today Junior was displaying all the unlovely characteristics of a spoilt only child. No matter how many titbits he received, he kept squawking for more, his mouth stretched wide as he beat wings not yet strong enough for flight. His poor parents looked so harried that Sam had to laugh.

When Richard arrived, she was able to greet him with a real smile; and on their way to pick up Amanda, whom Richard had offered to bring to save their host the trip, she gave him an account of the family drama, complete with an imitation of Junior which had them both laughing when they drew up to the imposing Marlowe residence.

Amanda wasn't quite ready, and Mrs Marlowe graciously invited them in to wait, ushering them into the family room, where Mr Marlowe was sitting with the Sunday papers. Sam moved in different circles from the well-to-do, socially active Marlowes and rarely saw them to speak to. A few minutes in their company was enough to remind her why she had no reason to regret their infrequent meetings, and to wonder for the first time if Amanda might be more to be pitied than blamed. The Marlowes judged everyone, and everything, by the twin standards of money and status. Sam was reasonably acceptable in their eyes because, although she lacked wealth, the Abbotts were An Old New England Family. Richard passed because he had gone to the right university and medical school, and because doctors could be expected to end up in one of the higher tax brackets.

Now that she thought about it, Sam couldn't remember hearing anything about the Marlowes objecting when Amanda had decided to marry a man older than her father. Stuart Thompson's enormous wealth and equivalent social standing had probably been more than enough to blind them to any drawback to the match. With parents like that, it was no wonder that Amanda had grown up with a warped sense of values.

Amanda finally made her entrance, dressed in a white sundress that showed off her careful tan. If her greeting to Sam lacked much warmth, it also lacked any tinge of Wednesday night's nastiness.

When she meekly climbed into the back seat of
the car, instead of finding some excuse to sit in
the front with Richard, Sam decided that there
was at least a remote possibility that Richard was
right, and Amanda had changed in the past year.
After all, her behaviour the other night might
have been caused by jealousy; even nice women
could turn nasty with that provocation. Perhaps
she was allowing her natural sympathy for anyone
afflicted with parents like the Marlowes to affect
her judgment, but if Simon could reveal a few—a
very few—redeeming qualities, maybe Amanda
would surprise her, too.

The old McDaniels estate, as the property was
still known in Westfield, was a couple of miles
south of the town proper. The short trip was
fully taken up in arguing about the logic of
calling a property by the name of a former owner.
And Sam's carefully polite attitude towards
Amanda thawed into natural friendliness as
Amanda joined her in defending the country
custom against the suburban-bred Richard, who
maintained that the habit led to more confusion
than it prevented.

A winding drive led to the house, which sat on
about thirty acres of grounds. Except for a strip
on either side of the drive and an area of lawn and
gardens around the house, the land, originally
cleared for farming, had been allowed to grow
wild; and trees of a respectable size were now
taking over from scrub growth. The original
stone farmhouse, built in the 1700s, had been
added to and altered to create a charming twenty-
room 'manor house,' which sat on a slight rise,
shaded by several large old oaks and maples. Old

Miss McDaniels, the last of the family, had lacked the money to keep up such a large place, and the last time San had been out here, the house had been starting to show the effects. Today, however, the paintwork gleamed whitely and the windows sparkled, while the shrubbery had been pruned, and the ivy discouraged from its attempts to take over the house.

'Quite a place,' commented Richard as he followed the branch of the drive which swung around in front of the house. 'And here's the Baron ... er ... the owner at the door to greet us.'

He just grinned when Sam hissed, 'Richard!' at him and got out of the car to shake hands with Simon before coming around to open Sam's door.

'Samantha, Amanda,' Simon greeted in his usual abrupt way. Like Richard, he was wearing slacks and a sports shirt, and Sam decided that he looked younger, but even more physically imposing. 'Come inside and say hello to Gran— she waiting in the living-room. Then I'll give you a quick tour of the house, if you're interested.'

'I'm dying to see it,' Amanda enthused. 'The outside looks marvellous! I'd forgotten what an impressive place this is.'

The living-room opened off to the right of the large entry hall and extended back to french doors leading on to a large, balustraded terrace. Mrs Radnor's slight figure was perched on a wing-back chair, her feet placed neatly together on a footstool to accommodate her lack of inches. Her back was firmly erect, as always, and her white hair was neatly confined in a severely styled french twist. But her brown eyes were sharp and lively, and her lips curved in a welcoming smile.

'Gran, this is Amanda Marlowe,' Simon told her, leading Amanda forward. 'And of course you know Samantha and Richard.'

'How do you do, Miss Marlowe? I believe I've met your father,' Mrs Radnor said with a nod, before turning to greet the other two less formally. 'Simon tells me that you've found a new nurse,' she said to Richard.

'Starting Monday,' he nodded.

'A good thing, too,' she told him severely. 'The last time I was in, the two of you were running around like chickens with their heads cut off!'

'You're just annoyed because you didn't get a chance to gossip with Sam,' Richard told her teasingly.

'I'm going to show our guests some of the work that's been done on the house before we go out to the pool,' interposed Simon. 'Do you want to join us?'

Mrs Radnor shook her head. 'I'd just slow you down. You go ahead, we'll have time to chat a while later.'

'I hope you can work up good appetites this afternoon,' Simon said wryly as he led the way across the hall to show them the small lift which had been installed for his grandmother. 'Gran and Mrs Gessner, our housekeeper, have planned a banquet masquerading as afternoon tea in your honour.'

From the hall he took them through a formal dining room, his study, an informal sitting-room, and a fair-sized breakfast room. The dining-room, like the living-room, had an oriental rug on a gleaming wood floor and mostly eighteenth-century-style furniture, though the period look was not followed slavishly in either room. In the sitting-room the floor was covered in wall-to-wall carpeting, and the brightly patterned upholstered furniture was clearly chosen for comfortable lounging. The breakfast-room had light, modern furniture that almost disappeared among a profusion of plants of all sorts and sizes. Sam viewed this display with approval, but her favourite room was Simon's study with its bookshelf-covered walls, old-fashioned oak pedestal desk, and oversized armchairs, just right for curling up in.

When she saw the kitchen, though, Sam almost changed her mind. Done in golden yellow, orange, and touches of green, the large but homey room was outfitted with every modern convenience known to man. Even Amanda's eyes brightened. While the men watched tolerantly, the two women investigated all the gadgets and looked over the separate pantry, the laundry room, and the suite for live-in help, which opened off the kitchen. The suite was presently unused, Simon explained, because Mrs Gessner used one of the upstairs bedrooms, so that his grandmother wasn't left alone at night when he was away on business.

After the women had satisfied their curiosity, Simon took them down to the basement to show them a well-equipped gym with attached sauna and a large workroom—'Where I play mad inventor,' he told them, as they looked around with respectful bewilderment at a scattering of electronic debris.

Here the tour ended, Simon dismissing the second floor as 'the usual collection of bedrooms and baths.' Sam would have liked to take a peep anyway, but she swallowed her disappointment politely. Simon's dismissal might, after all, have been motivated by a natural feeling that bedrooms were private, rather than by a man's failure to appreciate that most women would happily inspect closets and cupboards in a strange house, much less bedrooms and baths.

When they came up from the basement, he took Richard off to the cabana by the pool, and the two women went to change in the suite off the kitchen. It had occurred to Sam that the new Amanda might have been concocted for Richard's benefit, but when the old version failed to reappear as soon as they were alone, she relaxed and joined Amanda in enthusing over the house.

'I'll have to remember to ask Simon who did it for them,' Amanda remarked as she checked her eye make-up in the mirror. 'Mummy is looking for someone to re-do the living-room.'

Sam, who had not worn eye make-up for fear of ending up looking like a raccoon, made a mental note to invest in a waterproof brand of mascara for such occasions before answering, with only a touch of irony, 'Fom what Mrs Radnor has told me, they mostly "did" it themselves.'

'How amazing!'

Amanda sounded genuinely surprised and admiring of such a sturdy, pioneer, do-it-yourself approach, and Sam reflected that the idea of decorating your home yourself could very well be a novel one for someone raised in the Marlowes' circle.

Going out into the kitchen, they found Mrs Gessner, who had been upstairs during the tour. She greeted them in German-accented English and, in answer to Sam's query, told them, 'You have the path out of the door to follow the pool to reach,' then stood there beaming all over her round, apple-cheeked face.

Sam beamed back—it would have taken a real effort of will not to—and was strongly reminded of Santa Claus's wife. Mrs Gessner's hair was light brown instead of white, but she, too, was short and round, with a tidy bun on top of her head, bright brown eyes, and a cheerfully bustling air.

The path led down beside the living-room terrace and then around a hedge, to bring them out by a large, irregularly shaped swimming pool, landscaped to look like a natural pond and situated to give a view out over the surrounding countryside. The pool was encircled by a flagstone apron dotted with redwood lounger chairs, and off to one side was the cabana, whose exterior of unpeeled logs blended into the trees which bordered the area on one side.

'Quite something, isn't it?' Richard called from the pool. 'Come and join us when you're done gawking. The water feels great!'

Simon, who was treading water in the deep end, spoke up then. 'I hate to ruin Richard's fun, but as your negligent host, I feel it only fair to warn you that I forgot to turn the heating unit on this morning, and rainwater from last night has lowered the temperature a good bit.'

'In that case I think I'll lie in the sun for a bit

first,' Sam remarked, heading towards one of the lounger chairs.

'I'm going in now,' announced Amanda. 'Richard has earned himself a ducking.' She dropped her bag on a lounger, stripped off her lacy cover-up to reveal what there was of her turquoise maillot, and dived cleanly into the pool.

As she watched Richard's head disappear under the water a second later, Sam, who had been amazed by Amanda's willingness to ruin her hairdo, remembered that she had been a champion swimmer in her early teens. Either she had retained an indifference to water-soaked hair, or she was aware that no man was going to be looking at the top of her head while she was wearing that bathing suit.

While she had been watching Richard and Amanda, Sam had failed to notice that Simon had got out of the pool. But now he was coming right towards her and was quite impossible to miss. The fewer clothes he wore, the bigger he looked, she decided nervously. But in spite of his almost massive build, he had the sure-footed grace of a man who was fast, as well as strong, and who kept himself in top condition. That gym obviously wasn't just for show, she thought, before her eyes seemed to get tangled in the dark hair curling across the expanse of his muscular chest.

The Baron's sardonic voice freed her gaze. 'Let me help you out of that beach robe you're clutching,' he offered, or rather, stated.

Sam started and looked up, then struggled to fight back a blush as she met the mocking look in his eyes. The next instant, however, the mockery was replaced by the charming, crooked grin which had so surprised her the other day. 'I promise not to leer,' he told her, 'or not openly, at any rate.'

'How noble of you,' she managed, giving him a small, rather shy smile in return as she dropped the hand which had been unconsciously gripping the neck of her robe and began to untie the belt.

The emerald green bikini was perfectly decent, but she still felt naked after Simon had helped her remove the robe, and she turned to face him.

'Very nice. I like the colour,' he remarked calmly. 'I'll get you a beach towel to put over the chair cushions—the synthetic material tends to stick to you in this heat.'

And he walked away towards the cabana, leaving her staring after him in confusion. Somehow he always managed to throw her off balance, and it just wasn't fair, Sam thought plaintively. She had stared at his bare chest as if she had never seen one before, while he seemed more interested in her suit than in her shape!

A wolf whistle interrupted her thoughts. 'I like the view, Sam!' called Richard, giving her an appreciative grin.

It might have been a coincidence that Amanda chose that moment to splash water in his face, but Sam was inclined to doubt it. As she watched a laughing, protesting Amanda try to avoid a retaliatory ducking, however, she was less inclined to doubt that Richard's 'real' Amanda existed.

She was still watching the two in the pool when Simon returned, carrying several towels. He glanced at her sharply, but made no comment as he deposited the extra towels on a nearby table, then shook one out to cover Sam's lounger. As she thanked him and sat down, he picked up another, spread it over a neighbouring chair, and settled down beside her.

'I'll be fine if you want to go back in the water,' offered Sam, trying to sound casual.

Apparently she wasn't too successful. 'Relax, Samantha, I won't bite,' he assured her with lazy amusement. 'How do you like my artificial natural pool?'

'Er—very much,' she answered, her colour heightened by his comment. 'This design adds to the scenery instead of detracting from it.'

'Not as much as you do in that bikini,' he said, looking her over appreciatively, but without any offensiveness.

Sam finally began to relax. Perhaps he took his role as host seriously and really intended to behave today. 'I thought you promised not to leer,' she dared to tease.

'Only while you were taking your robe off. What's the point of giving a pool party if I can't leer at the female guests?'

'And here I thought we'd been invited because you wanted good company and scintillating conversation!' she mourned, sitting forward slightly to release the catch on the lounger and let the back down flat. 'I think I'll work on tanning my back and sulk for a while.' She shifted to her stomach and stretched out flat.

'I'm very good at putting sunscreen on backs,' Simon suggested.

Sam lifted her head to look at him, saw that he was teasing, and grinned. 'That one went out with, "Would you like to see my etchings?"'

He shrugged, causing a play of muscles beneath his tanned skin that Sam's eyes followed with unconscious fascination. 'I know, but I've been working so hard building up Radcom that I haven't had a chance to keep up on the latest seduction techniques,' he told her, the corners of his mouth turning up in a faint smile.

'Anyone can see that you've been wearing yourself to a frazzle,' she agreed ironically, running her eyes over him. Simon seemed to tense as she did so, and when she looked up, his eyes were partially hooded by dark lashes. For some reason her breathing suddenly quickened, and she felt her face heat up. Then his lashes lifted and he smiled.

'I can see I'm wasting my time trying to pry a little sympathy out of you. What happened to the soft feminine hand soothing a tired man's brow?'

'The woman attached to the hand wised up!' The heat in her face was subsiding, but she wondered what in the world was wrong with her. Simon was behaving very well, so she couldn't blame her reaction on him.

At that moment, the well-behaved Simon was thinking that things were progressing nicely. Samantha had to realise that Richard was still strongly attracted to Amanda, but she had looked thoughtful, rather than hurt or jealous as she had watched them in the pool. He had suspected the other night that she viewed marriage to Richard mainly as a safe, suitable arrangement, and now he was convinced of it.

Simon was nobody's fool, and it hadn't taken him long to put together the story of the car accident with Samantha's subsequent behaviour and arrive at certain conclusions. Part of Samantha—including the passion he sensed in her—had been in hiding since the accident; and though her reaction was understandable, it was more than time for someone to lure the hidden part of her out of retreat. Until she accepted that she would not be marrying Richard, his options were limited, but he was content for now to work on overcoming her distrust and encouraging her growing awareness of him as a man.

'Hey, Sam!' Richard's call broke the thoughtful silence which had fallen over the two recumbent figures. 'You and I have just challenged Simon and Amanda to a game of water polo.'

Sam turned her head to stare forbiddingly at him as he stood in the water holding what looked like a red plastic volleyball. 'Whatever possessed "us" to do that?'

'I need reinforcements,' he replied, with a meaningful look. 'Amanda's swimming circles around me.'

Time to play loving almost-fiancée, Sam thought in amusement. 'Be right there!'

As she sat up, Amanda called, 'Come on, Simon, you can't let these two gang up on me!'

Sam couldn't help thinking how appropriate Amanda's plea was; but when she glanced over to see if Simon was coming and caught the wicked gleam in his eye, she stopped thinking and started edging hurriedly over to the far side of her lounger. She was a bit too slow. Simon stood and scooped her up almost in one swift, effortless movement.

'Simon, don't you dare!' she protested as he

walked to the edge of the pool. She fastened her arms around the strong column of his neck and hung on, determined not to be tossed in.

'Take a deep breath, little cat,' he said in a low voice, the wicked gleam even more pronounced as he gazed down into her bright emerald eyes. Then his arms tightened around her, and he stepped off the edge.

Sam gasped as the chilly water hit her overheated skin. The water wasn't over Simon's head, but he purposely let them both go all the way under before he stood up straight. For an instant Sam just clung tighter to the warmth of his body, then she struggled away from his loosened hold.

'Rainwater, my f-foot!' she shivered. 'You've b-been dumping ice c-cubes in here!'

'Come over here, sweetheart,' laughed Richard. 'We'll start the game, and you'll soon warm up.'

For twenty minutes the battle raged up and down the pool, with Amanda and Simon drawing steadily ahead. Sam, as the shortest, had to work the hardest to keep up, and when Simon called a time out, she crawled out of the pool and collapsed on her lounger with a groan. Amanda dropped into the chair Simon had been using, and the men went off to the cabana to get cold drinks out of the small refrigerator inside.

'Are you going to survive?' asked Amanda in an amused, but friendly, tone.

Sam opened one eye. 'Just getting my second wind,' she explained.

'It occurs to me that the men are hogging the ball,' Amanda said thoughtfully.

'It occurred to me the second time one of them

swam right over me to grab it,' Sam replied feelingly.

'Have you ever noticed how hard it is in a crowd to avoid running into people's elbows occasionally, or tripping over someone's foot from time to time?' asked Amanda, still sounding thoughtful.

Sam's mouth slowly curved into a broad grin. 'And men can be so clumsy sometimes.'

'You take care of Richard, and I'll handle Simon,' Amanda suggested. 'That way they can't call a foul.'

Sam, who was just as happy not to tackle Simon anyway, readily agreed, and they were sitting back discussing bathing suit styles when the men returned with the drinks.

Richard sat down on the end of Sam's lounger and handed her a glass. 'You look like a waterlogged cherub,' he said, reaching out to give a friendly tug on one of the damp curls that were already springing back on her head. He laughed when she stuck out her tongue at him.

Simon, who had pulled up another chair beside Amanda's, looked from her to Sam and remarked, 'A Botticelli cherub and a Titian Venus—we seem to have collected a couple of Old Masters, Richard. I wonder how much we could get for them at auction?'

'Do you hear any odd oinking noises?' Sam asked Amanda innocently.

Amanda had been watching Richard with shadowed eyes, but she managed a smile and said, 'It has always seemed to me that male chauvinists bray more often than they oink.'

Sam burst out laughing, as Simon grinned and

Richard protested vociferously. Nobody could change this much; clearly Amanda had just been hiding her best qualities all these years!

When the water polo game resumed, the men at first assumed that the women had returned to the fray with renewed zest and had become over eager as a result. There was, after all, no benefit to Amanda in jabbing Simon in the solar plexus, or to Sam in sticking out her foot just in time to send Richard splashing flat on his face. Finally, however, it dawned on them that they were being sabotaged by their own partners.

'We've been had,' announced Richard with a scowl.

'I'm afraid so,' Simon agreed, eyeing the women, who were both starting to edge over to the nearest side of the pool for a quick getaways. 'You take Amanda, she's closer to you.'

Sam was halfway over the side when she was caught and pulled back by two large hands. 'Now, Simon,' she pleaded laughingly, 'it was only a—Simon!'

He had shifted his hold and was now lifting her up over his head. A second later she went flying to land with a resounding splat, sending waves of water spraying out in all directions. The waves collided with an identical set fanning out from where Amanda had landed.

'Archimedes was right,' Simon was remarking to a grinning Richard as the women resurfaced, 'a body does displace its own volume when placed in water.'

'Placed!' yelled Sam in outrage after a hasty check to make sure that both halves of her suit were intact and properly arranged. 'I'll place you!' Duckdiving under, a moment after Amanda, she headed for Simon's legs.

With equal accord the men decamped in opposite directions. The chase did not last long: Amanda, who could outswim all of them, soon caught up to Richard; and Simon only retreated to a point where he could stand, but Sam could not. She came in at an angle and lunged, catching him around the neck and trying to use the weight of her body to pull him under. Unfortunately, Simon didn't budge, and she was left dangling from his neck.

'No need to fling yourself at me, sweetheart. A gentle hint will do,' he mocked.

Sam glared into laughing eyes inches from her own and tried to move away. However, the momentum of her lunge had carried her body against his, and every move she made seemed only to increase the embarrassing intimacy of their contact. The sound of shared laughter indicated that Amanda and Richard had declared a truce, and Sam wanted to get disentangled before their attention turned this way.

In addition, not all the heat in her body or increase in the rate of her pulse could be attributed to embarrassment. With a sense of shock she realised that the explanation for her odd behaviour today was all too obvious; while her mind was still reserving judgment, her body had apparently made an arbitrary decision in Simon's favour. This realisation made her even more anxious to remove herself from his immediate vicinity.

'Don't just stand there grinning—do something!' she hissed. Then, as a Baron-like glint appeared in his eyes, she hastily specified, 'Help me get back on my feet.'

To her relief he placed his hands on her waist and started walking them towards the shallow end. 'You modern women,' he complained, his expression a perfect portrayal of long-suffering disapproval. 'I'm perfectly willing to support us both, but you have to be independent!'

Trying to keep her mind off the brush of his legs against hers as he moved through the water, Sam replied in the same spirit, 'We just want to be able to stand on our own two feet!' She managed to keep from sighing with relief as her feet actually did touch bottom just then.

Simon laughed and finally released her before turning towards Richard and Amanda, and Sam got a few needed moments to recuperate.

Fortunately, the rest of the afternoon passed in a lazy mix of swimming, sunning, and minimal physical contact. Sam managed to join in the conversation occasionally, but most of the time she concentrated on adjusting to her new, and extremely disconcerting, awareness of Simon. Darn Kate and her talk about sex appeal! she thought resentfully as she discovered that her rebellious eyes had again wandered to the fascinating sight of Simon's muscular, sun-browned body.

The important thing, though, was to keep her head. She had listened to friends mooning over the oddest men because of physical infatuations, and she wasn't going to have her peace disrupted that way! These seizures seemed to pass as suddenly as they began. All she had to do was avoid any risky situations in the meantime—like close encounters in swimming pools. And she had her supposed forthcoming engagement to protect her, Sam reminded herself, giving Richard a look of such fondness that Simon's eyes narrowed as he caught it.

At half-past four the two couples separated to change for tea on the terrace. Sam and Amanda took turns using the shower and the hair drier which someone had thoughtfully left in the small bathroom, then made their way out to the terrace. The men were already there, talking with Mrs Radnor while Mrs Gessner finished loading a table with plates of small sandwiches, pastries, cookies, and cakes.

'Good grief!' muttered Amanda, surveying the assembled feast. 'I'm going to have to fast for a week after this!'

Sam, who suffered from a sweet tooth, nodded agreement but said wistfully, 'I suppose it would be gauche to ask for a doggy bag.'

Just then Richard saw them and stood up. 'We were beginning to think you two had got lost.'

'I think he missed you,' said Mrs Radnor, looking up from where she was sitting behind a tea table at the centre of a semi-circle of white wrought-iron chairs.

'He was just being driven crazy by the sight of all this lovely food that couldn't be touched until we got here,' Sam corrected with a grin as she took a seat by Richard, on the opposite side of Mrs Radnor from Simon.

The others laughed, including Richard, who cheerfully accepted teasing about his outsized appetite. But Mrs Gessner, who had already enthused to Mrs Radnor about the 'beautiful

Herr Doktor,' looked upon him with even greater approval.

'Is all good food, my cooking,' she assured him earnestly, before retreating into the house with her serving cart.

'Mrs Gessner is a cook in search of an enormous appetite,' Mrs Radnor remarked with a twinkle as she began pouring tea and coffee. 'Simon is a grave disappointment to her. I'm not sure she would have taken this job if she'd realised what a moderate eater he is.'

Simon passed a cup to Amanda before adding, 'She can't figure out why I'm not fading away before her eyes. I think she harbours dark suspicions that I fill myself with inferior food when I'm out of the house.'

'Well, I promise to do my best to make her feel appreciated,' Richard promised.

'You should all be hungry after the ruckus you were raising down at the pool,' Mrs Radnor told them. 'There are plates on the table, so help yourselves. Simon, you could get me a sandwich and a piece of that chocolate torte, if you would, please.'

Sam hid a smile, but her dimples were showing as she put down her cup and started towards the food table. Mrs Radnor's 'request' to Simon had been made in much the same autocratic tone he had used on her all too often recently. It was a pleasure to witness him on the receiving end for once.

'You look as if you'd just finished licking some stolen cream off your whiskers,' Simon's rough voice murmured in her ear as she stood at one end of the table, trying to decide where to begin.

Sam controlled a start and, in turning towards him, edged away a bit. 'Your grandmother is waiting for her food,' she reminded him, trying to keep her face straight—but not very hard.

He raised one eyebrow, then looked amused. 'I see. You enjoy hearing me ordered around,' he deduced.

'Well, you do tend to do a lot of that yourself,' she pointed out as she began to fill a plate.

'I explained about the Radnor managing disposition,' Simon reminded her. 'It's an inherited trait, I can't do a thing about it.' Sam gave him a look of disbelief, which he met with blandly raised eyebrows. 'Gran, on the other hand, picked it up by association. You could always try that. Just think of all the fun you could have ordering me around yourself.'

'Tempting as the thought is, I doubt if Richard would approve,' she answered lightly, 'so I'll just concentrate on ignoring your orders. That's an inherited Abbott trait.'

'Not following orders?'

'Refusing to be dictated to,' she corrected. 'We've been working on it since the Revolutionary War.'

Simon smiled, then glanced down and commented, 'If you eat everything on that plate, you'll be too full for rebellion.'

Sam followed his gaze, and her eyes widened with dismay. While they had been talking, she had unthinkingly continued to pick up samples of the feast laid out on the table, and her plate was now piled high. 'Oh, dear! I'll never eat all this. And if I could, I shouldn't.'

'But think how happy you'd make Mrs Gessner,' Simon said.

'Yes, and I could roll right home, instead of having to go in the car,' she retorted.

In the end she did come close to clearing her plate, and when Richard suggested a stroll around the gardens, she groaned and shook her head. 'I'm going to have to rest for a while before I try moving,' she said plaintively.

'You and Amanda go ahead and explore,' suggested Simon. 'I'll stay here and keep Gran company while Samantha is recovering.'

After Richard and Amanda had gone off, Mrs Radnor remarked, 'That young woman is certainly an improvement on her father.'

Sam agreed and then looked thoughtful. 'She seems to have changed a lot in the past year.'

'I imagine that getting married and divorced in a little over a year would have some effect on anybody,' Mrs Radnor said drily.

'If she hadn't been blinded by his money, she could have found out easily enough beforehand that Stuart Thompson has a reputation for being rough on women—physically and emotionally,' Simon put in with a cynical twist to his mouth.

Sam's first reaction was that it was no wonder Amanda seemed different. The second was a sudden conviction that the cynicism which she so disliked in Simon was primarily directed against women. Could that be part of the reason for her antagonism towards him—that she had unconsciously sensed his attitude?

She had thought him arrogant, but though he definitely wasn't lacking in confidence, he showed no signs of self-importance. Perhaps what she had labelled arrogance was a disdain for women. Certainly he seemed to have no sympathy for Amanda, and though Sam didn't approve of marrying for money, it did sound as if Amanda might have got more than she deserved.

CHAPTER FOUR

JUST then, Mrs Gessner came out of the house. 'Mr Daniel Smith on the telephone is calling, Mr Radnor.'

Simon sighed and got up. 'Thank you, Mrs Gessner. Excuse me, Gran—Samantha. This may take a while, I'm afraid.'

As he disappeared through the french doors into the living-room, Mrs Radnor sniffed disapprovingly. 'Business, always business. The boy is thirty-five years old, and all he has to show for it is that silly company! His grandfather was a settled family man long since at his age.'

'People are marrying later these days, you know,' Sam pointed out, hiding a smile at the reference to Radcom. 'Simon still has plenty of time to start a family.'

As she spoke, an image formed in her mind of a sturdy little boy with curly brown hair and hazel eyes. The image wavered and broke when Mrs Radnor snorted.

'It's not so much time I'm worried about as lack of inclination. He made his fortune too early—had more money than he knew what to do with before he was much past twenty-five—and ran into too many greedy women who cared more for the money than for him. Soured him on marriage.'

That could explain his lack of sympathy for Amanda, Sam thought. But she couldn't believe that a few encounters with greedy women, however disillusioning, were sufficient to cause the deep-seated cynicism she sensed in him. Of course, it was nothing to do with her, but it would be interesting to know . . .

'I want him to find a nice girl like you and start a family,' Mrs Radnor was saying. 'He's got a strong protective urge, just like his grandfather, and he needs someone to look after besides an old lady with a bad heart. He'd be a good husband, like my Will was, too.'

The look in her eye as she spoke was making Sam nervous. 'Actually, I've been seeing a good deal of Richard lately,' she began tentatively.

'So Simon tells me,' Mrs Radnor said tartly. 'I don't know what foolishness you and the doctor are up to, young lady, but now that I've seen you together, I know it's not marriage! It's plain as the nose on your face that he's got his eye on the Marlowe girl, and I haven't seen much sign that you object.'

Sam opened her mouth to say something—she wasn't sure exactly what—when Mrs Radnor added, 'Oh, I won't give you away. Truth to tell, I'm pleased to see you cut up a bit . . .'—shades of Kate, Sam thought ruefully—'. . . besides, one of these days, I'm going to take great pleasure in telling that grandson of mine that he's not as smart as he thinks he is. Men need to be taken down a peg or two every so often.'

Sam grinned. 'I couldn't agree more! But . . . will you wait until I give you the all-clear sign?'

'Don't fret about that. I'm in no rush.'

'No rush about what?' asked Simon from behind them, causing Sam to jump visibly.

HUNTER'S SNARE 83

'If you leave your guests to take business calls, you can't expect us to repeat the conversation for your benefit,' Mrs Radnor told him as he came around to sit down beside her.

He sighed and stretched out his legs, crossing them at the ankle. 'You see how she bullies me?' he complained to Sam. 'No proper respect for the man of the house.'

'Yes, and it does my heart good,' Sam replied promptly, bringing a gleam of laughter into his eyes.

'You picked the wrong place to go for sympathy,' his grandmother said with a chuckle. 'Sam's got too much sense.'

'She's just feeling brave because you're here to protect her,' stated Simon, surveying Sam under half-closed lids, his mouth quirked up in a lazy smile.

Sam swallowed and hurriedly looked away. Oh, for the happy days when she had had her antagonism to protect her! she thought despairingly.

That evening as she got ready for bed, Sam was still trying to come to terms with the change in her relationship to Simon. Or rather, in her reaction to him, she corrected herself. A change in the relationship implied that Simon was aware of a difference, which she devoutly hoped he was not!

Up until today she had been certain that her virtue was quite safe from the Baron's wicked wiles. Now her confidence had received a jolt. Not that she felt herself to be in imminent danger, but she wasn't used to feelings that she couldn't control, and she didn't like the vul-

nerable feeling it gave her. What was more, she
was beginning to enjoy Simon's company, which
made the situation even more dangerous.

Thank heaven for Richard, Sam thought.
Given time, this aberration would fade away, or
she would learn to control it. Meanwhile, she
would avoid Simon as much as possible; there
was no point in taking risks, however small.
History, after all, was clear on one point: when it
came to maidens, barons were more given to
declaring open season than to efforts at conser-
vation.

Her plans made, Sam went off to sleep, happily
unaware that Simon had already made plans of
his own, which did not include allowing her to
avoid him.

During the next week it seemed to her that she
saw Simon at least once every day. If he and
Richard hadn't arranged a double date, he was
stopping by her house with samples of Mrs
Gessner's cooking sent by his grandmother. She
could take no exception to his behaviour, but
given his effect on her, poor Sam ended up
brooding about whether it was possible to be
besieged and ambushed at the same time.

She considered telling Richard that she could
do without the double dates, but since they were
a perfect way for him to spend time with Amanda
without committing himself, she didn't have the
heart. Although she was more and more
convinced that the change in Amanda was
genuine, she could understand and sympathise
with his desire to take things slowly.

On Saturday night, what Kate insisted upon

calling the 'mixed-up doubles' went out for dinner and then to Janson's again for dancing. Sam was not overjoyed by the second half of the programme. As she had anticipated, Richard danced with Amanda at least half the time, which left far too many dances free for Simon.

But why always the slow numbers? she groaned to herself as she went into his arms for the fourth time. She was definitely going to have a word with Richard about this. The worst part was that everything was getting twisted around. There had been a moment at the end of the last dance when she had actually been reluctant to move away from Simon because she felt so secure in his arms—and this time she didn't even have the excuse of a migraine. How could she possibly think of security when her pulse was racing, and she felt as if she were melting inside?

'They make a good-looking couple, don't they?'

Sam glanced up, then followed Simon's gaze over to where Richard and Amanda were dancing, the golden and red heads close together. 'And I suppose Richard and I don't?' she suggested sweetly.

'Personally, I find blond on blonde a little bland. The red hair adds interest. Of course, being dark myself, I prefer fair-haired women,' he finished.

'You're too kind,' Sam said awfully.

Simon laughed, then said seriously, 'You aren't going to make things difficult for them, are you, Samantha? You must realize by now that whatever Richard feels for you, his feelings for Amanda are much stronger.'

What's between Richard and me is our business,' replied Sam, refusing to meet his eyes. She heard him mutter, 'Stubborn little mule!' under his breath, but to her relief he said nothing more for the rest of the dance.

During the band's next break Simon sprang another of his surprises. 'I'm planning to give a party soon,' he mentioned casually. 'Sam told me that a lot of people would like to see what we've done with the house, and I have some social debts to pay.'

'What fun!' Amanda exclaimed. 'What size party, and when do you plan to have it?'

'A couple of hundred or so, and it will be two weeks from today.'

'That doesn't allow much time for preparation,' Sam said doubtfully. 'And won't it be too much for your grandmother?'

'Between my office staff and Mrs Gessner, Gran has nothing to do but approve the arrangements. Most of the preparations are well in hand already. But to make sure she takes it easy at the party, I would appreciate it if you and Amanda would act as deputy hostesses.'

Well, I walked right into that one, Sam thought. But naturally she agreed, though with less enthusiasm than Amanda.

During the rest of the evening she managed to arrange things so that she only had one more slow dance with Simon. But the traitorous, reckless Sam who seemed to be emerging more strongly every day allowed him to hold her far too closely and made no objection when he put both his arms around her and turned the dance into a swaying embrace.

The next day, freed from the Baron's regrettable influence, she was appalled by her own poor showing. 'I'm the descendant of generations of typical New Englanders—moral fibre and unbending principles galore. Most of them wouldn't have recognised temptation if it jumped up and bit them. What happened to me?' she moaned to Kate.

'All New Englanders couldn't have been like that, or Hawthorne would never have written *The Scarlet Letter*,' Kate pointed out.

'Oh, terrific. You're such a comfort to me.'

'Then there were all the stocks and the ducking stools,' she added, warming to the subject. 'There must have been plenty of normal people around.'

'Will you be serious?' demanded Sam, trying to keep from laughing.

Kate laughed. 'If you insist.' Then she suggested, 'Why don't you stop this pretence with Richard? You wouldn't have to see so much of Simon Radnor then, and you seem to be convinced now that Richard is safe with Amanda.'

'I am,' Sam agreed. 'But Richard wants to carry on a little longer, and I wouldn't feel right deserting him at this stage. Anyway, the pretence is protection for me, too.'

'All you would have to do is refuse to see Radnor, and you wouldn't need protection,' said Kate.

'Ha!'

'Besides, continuing with these double dates could cause other problems.' Kate paused and then intoned ominously, 'There is talk in the village.'

'Uh-oh! What are they saying?'

'General opinion seems to be that that snake-in-the-grass Amanda Marlowe is either planning to snare Simon Radnor for his money, or using him as a cover while she tries to steal that nice Dr Bohlen from poor Sam Abbott.'

Sam was well aware of the village propensity for minding everyone else's business, but she had had so much on her mind during the past week or so that she hadn't stopped to consider what the gossips were making of all the goings-on. Now, though, she wondered how she could have missed a problem that should have been obvious as soon as she began to entertain hopes of a happy ending for Richard and Amanda.

Amanda's past attitude and behaviour had not exactly endeared her to her neighbours, and many would be ready to believe that she had 'stolen' Richard from her. That would certainly be unpleasant for all of them. Unfortunately, at the moment Sam could not come up with a good solution. And Richard did no better when she consulted him, after mulling the matter over. He did agree, however, that they would be wise to avoid double dates for a while in the hope that the gossip would die down a bit, a decision which proved easy to carry out when Simon was suddenly called away on business.

When she heard that Simon would be away for at least a week, Sam was greatly relieved. A whole week undisturbed by worrying about what the Baron would do next! But after a couple of days enjoying the peace and quiet, she realised to her dismay that she was bored. The daily routine that had kept her happily satisfied for years seemed flat and unexciting. Could she actually be missing Simon's disruptive presence?

No sooner had the alarming thought presented itself than Sam sought to argue it away. As far as she was concerned, Simon ought to carry a label reading 'Caution: Hazardous to Your Health'. He might be enjoyable company at times, but he had a dangerously insidious effect on her. He undermined her self-control, confused her senses, and last night he had had the nerve to infiltrate her dreams. She was only too pleased that he had taken himself and his sex appeal elsewhere for a while!

Her defences aroused and on alert, Sam succeeded in quashing the ridiculous notion and turned her attention to the more prosaic problem of what she was going to wear to the party. Since John had received an invitation, Kate was faced with the same dilemma, and the two of them set out to the nearby city of Stamford one evening to do some serious shopping.

By the time they started home, Kate had bought a silky blue dress with a beautifully draped bodice and had talked Sam into buying a ruinously expensive strapless creation in aqua georgette.

'I should never have come shopping with you,' Sam complained as they left the parking lot. 'My bank account will never be the same, and neither will I after appearing in public indecently dressed!'

'That dress is not indecent, and you look terrific in it,' Kate said firmly.

The dress did, indeed, start at a respectable level, and no one could take exception to the gentle blouson top or the flowing skirt which ended just above the knee. The problem lay in the clever design that successfully camouflaged the elastic supporting the top; at first glance the dress appeared to be defying gravity.

A few days later, dressed for the party, Sam stood in front of her full-length mirror checking her appearance. Her cheeks were flushed, and her eyes were deep green with excitement—over the party, of course. If the feeling of anticipation had anything to do with seeing Simon for the first time in two weeks, Sam wasn't about to admit it. Certainly she would have denied to the death that she had found the courage to wear her new dress because she wanted him to see her at her best. Instead, she convinced herself that the triple-string pearl choker inherited from her great-grandmother lent an aura of Edwardian respectability to offset the dress's daring.

When Richard arrived to pick her up, his reaction was so positive that she was torn between pleasure and renewed doubts. They were stopping for Amanda, and while Richard went up to the house to fetch her, Sam gave the dress a couple of quick tugs to reassure herself that it was securely anchored.

Richard soon returned with a radiant Amanda, dressed in a one-shoulder dress in black and white printed silk, that swirled around her in a shifting caress as she moved.

'Samantha darling, what I can see of your dress looks positively shattering!' she said in greeting as she settled into the back seat.

Sam, who was becoming accustomed to Amanda's lapses into 'Socialese', turned to smile ruefully at her. 'It's already shattered my poise. I keep having to suppress the urge to hike it up.'

'Nonsense, darling! I recognise the designer, and his things never fall down—the price makes them too stiff.'

Sam gave a laughing groan at the pun. 'You have a point. And in case Richard was too stunned to tell you, you look fairly shattering yourself.'

When they arrived at the old McDaniels estate, a young man took Richard's keys and drove the car off to an improvised parking lot to one side of the house. One of the caterer's people let them in and directed them back to the sitting-room, where Mrs Radnor was waiting, dressed in a high-necked beige lace dress. Her usual severe hairdo had been softened, and Sam decided that she looked like a duchess, at least.

After greeting them, Mrs Radnor ordered, 'Sam, come over here where I can get a better look at that dress.' Sam went over obediently and twirled when commanded. 'Very clever,' pronounced Mrs Radnor after her examination. 'If I were forty years younger, I'd copy it.'

Sam smiled, relieved by the approval, then felt an odd prickle in the back of her neck and turned to look behind her. Simon was standing in the doorway, looking darkly handsome in a white dinner jacket. Their eyes met, and she felt her pulse give a sudden leap at the look in his. Then his gaze dropped, and his eyes narrowed abruptly.

'What the hell are you wearing, if I may use the term so loosely?' he demanded grimly. The others turned at the sound of his voice, but he ignored them, glittering hazel eyes impaling the unfortunate Sam.

The abrupt switch of mood, and the un-expectedness of his reaction, threw Sam off balance. 'A dress,' she answered literally in a small, breathless voice.

She wasn't trying to be funny, but her answer drew a choked laugh from Richard. Simon, however, was not in the mood to appreciate the humour of her reply. Caught unaware by a sudden and unfamiliar attack of jealous posses-siveness, he simply ignored Richard and con-tinued to scowl at Sam.

'There's nothing holding that damn thing up,' he rasped.

'Really, Simon! It's a marvellous dress,' Amanda objected. 'And Samantha looks won-derful in it.'

As Sam, eyes pricking with tears of hurt, cast her a look of gratitude, Mrs Radnor entered the fray. 'Amanda is right. Anyway, Sam has a perfect right to dress how she pleases,' she informed her grandson tartly.

'She's also going to please every man here under ninety,' he replied forbiddingly.

By this time Sam's hurt was turning to anger. Who was Simon to criticise her or play puritan? And what did she care about his opinion, anyway? 'The dress is perfectly secure; there are pieces of elastic all around the top,' she told him defiantly. 'I'd hardly wear a dress that was going to fall down!'

'It would be preferable if the elastic were more evident,' he retorted. Then he turned abruptly to Richard before she could reply. 'Come have a drink with me in the study. The ladies don't need us right now, and this evening looks like being more of a strain than I had anticipated.'

Sam glared at his retreating back, one part of her wanting to throw something at him, another wanting only a place to hide and have a good cry. Not that she would give him the satisfaction, after he had done his best to ruin the evening for her before it had even started!

'You mustn't mind Simon,' Mrs Radnor said after Richard had left, with a consoling pat on Sam's shoulder. 'Men get themselves into a tizzy over the silliest things. My Will didn't speak to me for three days after I had my hair bobbed, back in the twenties.'

'I thought for a moment he was going to order you home to change!' laughed Amanda.

'Well, he would have been in for a disappointment if he had,' Sam replied belligerently. At the same time it belatedly occurred to her that Richard should have come to the defence of the woman he was supposed to be in love with. Had Simon noticed this telltale failure? If Amanda had, she didn't appear surprised by it, Sam noted thoughtfully.

For the next half-hour, the three women went over the arrangements for the party. Then they paid a quick visit to the kitchen and to the marquee which had been put up nearby as a refreshment area.

Mrs Gessner was overseeing the food end, but Mrs Radnor suggested that Sam and Amanda might drop into the kitchen from time to time. 'People like to know that their efforts are appreciated, no matter how much they are being paid,' she added. 'I'll go back there later on, but you two could save me some steps by taking on that job in the meantime.'

A bar had been placed at one end of the terrace, and at the other end the band was setting up. Those who wanted to dance could use part of the terrace, or go down on the lawn below. The grounds were strung with lights, and some benches had been set around for people who wished to sit and talk away from the marquee area. Inside, the first floor was open for guests to view, but the doors to the basement and to the occupied bedrooms had been locked. 'Much simpler than finding polite ways to eject people who wander where they shouldn't,' Amanda approved.

When the guests arrived, the women would be offered the use of a guest bedroom set aside as a cloakroom, then everyone would be directed through the living-room to the terrace, where the Radnors would be receiving.

Around nine o'clock cars began pulling up to the house. Amanda was dispatched to retrieve the men from the study, while Sam got Mrs Radnor settled in a chair on the terrace, just outside the living-room.

'For once I can see an advantage to the doctors' lists of all the things I can't do,' Mrs Radnor remarked. 'Otherwise I'd have to stand here like a post for an hour wearing my feet out.'

Amanda returned with the men just ahead of the first guests. 'Let's go sample that Planter's Punch the caterer mentioned,' she suggested to Sam and Richard, as they moved away to allow the Radnors to greet the newcomers.

'High octane or regular, sir?' asked the bartender with a smile when Richard requested three glasses of punch.

'What's the difference?'

'High octane'll put hair on your chest.'

'Regular,' chorused Sam and Amanda.

Richard laughed. 'Well, I suppose that leaves me to sample the high octane!' After one swallow from the glass he received, he took a deep breath and said to the grinning bartender, 'Now I know how those Caribbean planters survived the heat— they fought fire with fire!'

As the terrace filled up, Amanda and Sam started to circulate among the guests, and Sam was soon grateful that she knew, and was known by, many of the people there. The reactions to her dress varied from curiosity among the women as to how it was constructed, to bemused fascination among the men. But although she did conduct more than one conversation with a man without his ever raising his eyes far enough to meet hers, she encountered more teasing offers than serious ones to view the darker areas of the grounds.

Around ten o'clock Sam made a quick trip to the kitchen and marquee, where everything was going smoothly. When she returned, she looked around for Richard and Amanda, whom she hadn't seen for a while. Neither was in sight, though she did see Amanda's parents and noted with amusement that Mr Marlowe was clearly enjoying the Planter's Punch. Earlier on she had thought that she had caught a glimpse of John and Kate, but they, too, were not in evidence at the moment.

Everything seemed to be going well, Sam

thought, leaning back against the balustrade and relaxing for a moment. The terrace was thronged with a crowd of gaily-dressed people, who were nearly drowning out the band with their talk and laughter; the bar was doing a brisk business; and small groups were wandering around the grounds and inspecting the interior of the house. The outside lights were now on, illuminating the lawn and gardens with a frosted white glow, and the air had cooled down to a level more comfortable for the men in their jackets and ties.

She was just thinking that she ought to check in with Mrs Radnor when she spotted Simon coming towards her. For a second she had an urge to turn and try to disappear into the crowd. She hadn't had much time to herself to think, but the hurt she had felt at his reaction to her dress had forced her to admit that she had wanted his approval. The thought both angered and distressed her, and she wanted nothing to do with Simon at the moment. But if he wished to speak to her, he would track her down, and she had no desire to start dodging about like a scared rabbit.

Straightening up, she awaited his approach, noting how he seemed to stand out from the crowd of guests with that look of restrained power. Even when her antagonism had been at full strength, she had been aware that women found him attractive, but now she was newly conscious of the little flutters, the sideways glances, that followed him.

'Gran has released me from my post. Come and start the dancing with me, Samantha,' he said with his usual abruptness, as he came up to her.

Whatever Sam was expecting, it wasn't an invitation to dance, and he had already taken her arm and started to lead her towards the band before she managed to object. 'Simon, you're supposed to ask a lady to dance and then wait for an answer,' she hissed at him. 'What if I don't want to dance?'

'Why do you think I didn't wait?' he murmured, nodding to people as they passed but refusing to be detained. 'If you aren't willing to accept a "no", then there's no point in waiting, is there?'

'Of all the arrogant . . .!'

They had reached the area in front of the band, which was playing a slow, romantic number, and he pulled her into his arms, cutting off her protest. 'I wasn't going to let anyone else dance with you until I could be sure that damn dress will stay where it's supposed to,' he growled into her ear.

Sam stiffened angrily.

'Relax, Samantha,' he whispered. 'I'm not going to start another argument. I've already received strict instructions from Gran on that subject.'

Sam didn't reply. She was preoccupied with fighting the shivery feeling inside that had started with the movements of his lips against her ear. This time she would not succumb. She would *not*, she told herself desperately, even as her body began to curve into his, and his arms tightened around her . . .

As the music drew to a close, Simon straightened and looked down into dreamy green eyes with a glint of satisfaction in his own. Then

his gaze slipped down over her shoulders to the
top of her dress. 'So far, so good,' he told her.
'You may dance, but don't stray out of the
lighted part of the grounds.'

Sam was still sputtering incoherently, to his
obvious amusement, when a young man with
whom she had gone to school approached
hesitantly to ask her to dance. Giving Simon a
smouldering look, she swallowed her outrage and
accepted with a smile.

A couple of dances and partners later, she
refused another invitation and went inside to visit
the bedroom set aside for the ladies to check on
her hair and make-up. As she passed through the
living-room, she saw Mrs Radnor holding court
on a sofa, attended by a small crowd of guests. An
enquiring glance drew a nod and a smile.
Nothing for her to do here.

On her way back outside, she took a detour
through the kitchen. A brief conversation with
Mrs Gessner revealed that Amanda had not been
by in over an hour, and Sam was wearing a slight
frown as she walked up the shallow steps to the
terrace. She would have sworn that Amanda took
social duties seriously, and she was puzzled by
this apparent laxity.

As she reached the terrace, however, she
spotted the missing Amanda off in a corner
talking to her parents. While Sam was still
watching, Mrs Marlowe suddenly enveloped her
daughter in a hug, and Mr Marlowe made some
remark with a pleased smile and started to walk
away. Amanda called to him and seemed to try to
catch his arm, but she was hampered by her
mother's embrace.

What was that about? Sam wondered. Looking around for Mr Marlowe, she saw him talking to the leader of the band. After a moment the leader nodded and signalled the group to stop playing.

'May I have your attention!' Mr Marlowe's voice boomed out over the noise of the crowd.

'What the . . .?'

Turning at the exclamation from beside her, Sam discovered Richard, holding two full glasses in his hands. 'Take these,' he ordered brusquely, pushing the glasses at Sam, who reached for them automatically. Then he plunged into the crowd towards Amanda, who now appeared to be arguing with her mother.

'May I have your attention!' Mr Marlowe repeated. 'I have a very happy announcement to make. I am pleased and proud to tell you that my daughter Amanda is engaged to marry Dr Richard Bohlen.'

Oh, my God! Sam thought blankly. What did that idiot think he was doing?

The sound of scattered, somewhat belated applause pulled her out of her shock, and her mind began working feverishly. Since she had last seen Richard and Amanda about an hour ago, they must have been off somewhere getting everything straightened out and settled between them. When they had returned, Amanda had obviously told her parents; and probably due to too much high-octane punch, Mr Marlowe had misplaced his social finesse. Even assuming he was unaware, or had forgotten, that Richard was supposed to be seeing her, not Amanda, it was too soon after Amanda's divorce for anything more than a discreet newspaper item of the 'planning to wed' variety. But the damage was done, and she had better do what she could to help.

Banishing her dismay from her mind, Sam put on an expression of pleased surprise and made her way up to Richard and Amanda, who were now receiving congratulations with distracted smiles. 'Amanda, I'm so glad!' she exclaimed, giving the other woman a hug.

Amanda clutched at her and whispered frantically, 'I couldn't stop him!'

Sam nodded slightly to show she understood before going on in a clear, slightly raised voice, 'I was wondering how we could give Richard a nudge, but he did pick a lovely night for a proposal.'

Scattered laughter greeted this comment, and Sam turned to Richard with more assurance. 'Finally got carried away by the moonlight, did you?' she teased, reaching up to kiss his cheek.

Richard joined in the louder laughter that followed, then bent down to return the kiss, whispering a heartfelt, 'Thank you!' before he straightened.

Having done what she could there, Sam made way for other people and moved off to circulate around the terrace, determined to make it clear to everyone she could that she was thrilled by the engagement of her two good friends. She soon ran into—or was tracked down by—two of the village's most notorious gossips, Mrs Bates and Miss Beasley. In Westfield rumours were said to be carried by little birds and the Bs!

Though Sam's had been aware of curious speculation lurking in the minds of the people she had been talking to, no one had quite had the nerve to come right out and question her about her own relationship with Richard. Miss Beasley repaired this omission.

'But Sam dear, we *all* thought that *you* and Dr Bohlen ... Well, you've been seeing so *much* of him recently, haven't you?' she asked, her thin nose visibly twitching as she waited for Sam's reaction.

Perhaps because of present urgency, a simple and effective way of countering any talk of Amanda stealing Richard had already occurred to Sam; however, she had hoped to avoid using it until she had had a chance to secure the co-operation of the other party. Too late now, though, she acknowledged ruefully as she gave Miss Beasley a look of surprise, artfully followed by one of amused comprehension.

'I see that all our double dates confused everyone,' she said with a smile. 'I was always with Simon Radnor, not Dr Bohlen. Maybe we should have made an announcement to——'

Sam was about to say 'to make it clear who was with whom', but Mrs Bates interrupted before she could finish. 'There! What did I tell you?' she exclaimed to Miss Beasley in her high, carrying voice, her round face beaming with pleasure at having got the best of her dearest friend and rival. 'Dr Bohlen has always been nutty on the Marlowe girl!'

She turned to Sam again. 'I think it would be marvellous if you and Mr Radnor did make an announcement tonight, too. Besides, with a good catch like Mr Radnor, you want to pin him down as quickly as possible,' she added with a wink.

'But I didn't——'

'And here's the lucky man now!' shrilled Mrs Bates, drowning out Sam's attempt at protest. 'Oh, Mr Radnor,' she rolled on, as Simon's arm fastened around a Sam who was now petrified with embarrassment and a sense of impending doom, 'Sam was just telling us that we can expect to hear wedding bells for the two of you before long.'

'No!' Sam gasped frantically with the diminished air left in her lungs after Simon's arm tightened brutally around her waist.

'Was she, indeed?' Simon replied in an ominously silky voice as Sam tried to get enough breath for another attempt at speech.

She was vaguely aware that someone else had joined their little group, but she didn't realise who it was until Miss Beasley, alertly spotting her chance to join in the conversation, gushed, 'I expect *you* were *thrilled* by the news, Mrs Radnor. Sam is *such* a nice girl. We're all *very* fond of her.'

Simon's arm tightened another notch, and Sam, happy by now to take any means of escape from this nightmarish scene, stopped trying to fight the faintness that was closing in on her. Everything began to slowly twirl around, and then the colours faded to grey . . .

CHAPTER FIVE

SAM moaned. She felt shaky and sick.

'Sam?'

Her eyes fluttered open to see Richard bending over her. As she stared up at him, everything came back to her. 'Oh, Richard, the Bs!' she groaned, shutting her eyes again.

She heard him move away and say to someone, 'Would you get a cup of tea with a good spoonful of sugar, and some of those little sandwiches, please?'

Opening her eyes again, she glanced around fearfully. She was lying on the leather couch in Simon's study and at the end of the couch, looming like Nemesis, stood Simon himself, with an expression which spoke so strongly of iron control that Sam was seriously alarmed. 'It w-was all a m-misunderstanding,' she rushed to explain.

'Not now, Samantha,' he ordered in a clipped voice. 'We'll talk later, when you're feeling better.'

With that sort of encouragement she might become a permanent invalid, Sam thought nervously. Then Richard was bending over her again.

'Good. You're getting some colour back in your face,' he announced with a smile. 'How are you feeling?'

'Very Victorian,' she replied, giving him a shaky smile in return.

Richard laughed. 'I know you didn't faint because your stays were pulled too tight, so what did bring it on?'

'Something similar,' Simon answered before she could speak. 'I was holding her so tightly that she couldn't breathe. When she tried to tell me so, I thought she was just attempting to get a word in between Mrs Bates and Miss Beasley.'

'And that's why you mentioned the Bs when you came to,' Richard said to Sam with a nod, apparently accepting this explanation.

When she opened her mouth to correct his misinterpretation, Simon got in before her again. 'I'll be more careful from now on. Samantha is very deceptive; I forgot how . . . delicate she is.'

The words sounded innocent enough, but Sam had the uncomfortable conviction that they weren't. She was growing more and more anxious to explain what had happened. 'It was——'

'Don't blame yourself too much, Simon,' Mrs Radnor interrupted from behind Sam, causing her to start. 'Sam isn't really delicate, but it isn't every day that a girl gets engaged. I'm sure that the excitement was a contributing factor.'

'But——'

'So it's true! Miss Beasley babbled something about that when she came to tell me Sam had fainted, but I didn't pay any attention,' Richard broke in.

Sam was opening her mouth for yet another try when Simon gave her such an intimidating look of warning that she meekly subsided. She had no idea why he wanted her to keep quiet, but her sense of self-preservation strongly recommended that she humour him for the moment.

'Well, congratulations,' Richard continued, shaking Simon's hand. 'You know, Amanda insisted that you two would end up together.'

'Never doubt a woman's intuition,' Amanda told him as she came in just then with a tray. 'The news has already reached the kitchen, by the way, and Mrs Gessner is in ecstasies at the thought of another permanent mouth to feed!'

She set down the tray on the table in front of the couch, and went on, 'Samantha darling, I do admire your flair for the unusual. I don't think I remember anyone ever announcing an engagement by passing out before. Were you overcome by joy, or by the sudden realisation of what you were taking on?' Sam had to smile, though she didn't dare look to see what effect Amanda's remarks were having on Simon. 'No, don't answer—you might incriminate yourself. Just drink your tea. Then we'll leave you alone for a family conference.'

'You should be all right now, Sam,' Richard agreed. 'Have a bite to eat, though, and sit quietly for a while.'

When they left a couple of minutes later, Sam was feeling much better able to face the 'family' conference. Mrs Radnor opened it.

'I'm not going to stay long, since I imagine you two have things to discuss,' she began, 'but I want you to know, Sam, that I couldn't be happier about the news, and I shall look forward to welcoming you into the family soon. I suspect that you hadn't planned to make the announcement tonight, but I think I can guess what happened.'

'You can?' asked Sam cautiously, after a quick

glance at Simon, which assured her that her part was still to say as little as possible.

'Oh, yes. I heard some of the talk after Amanda's father made that unfortunate announcement, and I imagine you just let out more than you intended to while trying to convince that Laurel and Hardy gossip team that Amanda hadn't snitched Richard out from under your nose.'

'The Bs do rather tend to grab the ball and run with it,' Sam replied with heartfelt understatement.

'Well, don't worry about it, dear,' the old lady told her. Then she added with a twinkle, 'And you've certainly assured a successful evening. How many parties can boast of two unexpected engagement announcements?'

Sam smiled back and hoped that her smile didn't look as sick as it felt.

'Now, Simon, take care of Sam,' his grandmother admonished as she got up. 'We don't want her fainting again.'

'Don't worry, Gran,' he assured her gently as he walked to the door and opened it for her. 'Why don't you go up soon? You've had a busy evening, and Amanda will take care of things until Sam and I get back out there.'

'All right, dear. I am a bit tired. I'll say goodnight to you both, then.'

Simon shut the door and locked it with a decisive click before turning to face Sam.

'Simon, I want to explain——'

'Be quiet and eat your sandwiches, Samantha,' he said in a dangerously soft voice. 'I'm going to have a drink. Then maybe I'll be able to listen to you without getting the urge to cut off your breath again.' And he turned to walk over to a cabinet concealing a small bar on the other side of the room.

Any appetite Sam might have had promptly disappeared. She had been right; Simon was furious. But why hadn't he just straightened out the mistake, or let her do so? And why was he so terribly angry in the first place? Surely he must realise that it was all an unfortunate mistake . . . or did he? Lost in thought, Sam reached out and picked up one of the fancy sandwiches on the plate in front of her.

At the bar Simon poured himself a Scotch and worked to bring his anger under control. Then, as he grew calmer, he admitted that he was more angry with himself than he was with Samantha. Recently he had begun to wonder if she might be one of the rare women like his grandmother who could be trusted not to succumb to the lure of money. He should have known better—in fact, he did know better—but he had still fallen into the trap.

Admittedly Samantha had not, like Amanda, been raised from the cradle to venerate wealth. Nor did she show any signs of greed for possessions. But he should have remembered that money could represent security, as well as status and possessions.

Simon frowned, staring down at the glass in his hand. To be fair, she had shown no interest in him, or his money, before this evening. Perhaps losing the secure future of marriage to Richard had brought this on. Judging by her attitude towards Richard and Amanda just now, she was neither surprised nor deeply hurt, but that did not mean that she wasn't upset. Maybe she had even started out pairing their names to stop gossip as Gran had suggested and then carried the idea further on impulse.

Yes, that made sense, he thought, the frown lifting. She just wasn't a good enough actress to have been misleading him completely all this time, hiding a grasping, deceitful nature. But how ironic if the Samantha he was trying to winkle out of her shell had emerged far enough to impulsively chance trapping him into marriage, he added, his mood lightening into wry humour. Well, he would have to make sure that she wasn't tempted to try anything like that again. A little acting of his own should do the trick. He would turn her own trap against her . . .

When Simon walked back over, he no longer appeared to be restraining himself from violence; however, his unyielding expression convinced Sam that the explanation she had arrived at for his anger was correct: Simon believed that she was one more greedy, conniving woman after his money. The misjudgment was both insulting and hurtful, but given his attitude towards women and the compromising situation, she supposed it was inevitable. And even if she wasn't greedy, she had connived with Richard—which Simon still was not aware of, she realised suddenly as he sat down across from her. But she couldn't tell him now; things were complicated enough as it was!

'Feeling better?' he asked silkily.

'I'll feel better when this mess is straightened out,' she answered bravely. 'Why did you stop me from speaking earlier?'

'We'll get to that in a minute. First, I want to hear about the "mess", as you so aptly call it.'

His tone was far from encouraging, but she took a deep breath and plunged in. 'I was telling the Bs that I was with you on our double dates, so that everyone wouldn't be down on Amanda for stealing Richard. Then Mrs Bates cut me off in the middle of a sentence and thought I was saying something I wasn't. And the next thing I knew, she was talking about an engagement.' Maybe you had to be there, she thought ruefully, as she noted his disbelieving expression.

'And of course, you didn't want to be so rude as to tell her she was wrong,' he said sarcastically, one eyebrow raised in the Baron's mocking look.

'You came up before I had a chance to,' she explained.

'Ah, yes. Mrs Bates was just advising you to nail down a good catch like me as soon as possible. Then she announced that we're going to be married soon,' he recalled smoothly. 'That must have been an interesting sentence she interrupted.'

'Mrs Bates is almost incapable of repeating anything without embellishments. Going from an engagement to an early wedding is nothing,' Sam explained, keeping her voice even with an effort. 'If you'd lived here longer, you'd know not to believe anything she or Miss Beasley said, even without embellishments, unless you'd checked the facts yourself. They don't mean any harm, but they love to gossip.'

'So the whole situation was an unfortunate misunderstanding,' stated Simon with a nasty smile, 'and it never occurred to you that since you couldn't marry Richard, you might as well settle for the security of a large fortune attached to a man you've just discovered you don't detest after all.'

'It *was* a misunderstanding,' Sam ground out, her cheeks now flushed with anger. 'The rest is all wrong—except possibly for the last part!'

Simon repressed a laugh at that shot. He discovered that in spite of lingering anger, he was beginning to enjoy himself. With her curls rumpled from lying on the couch and her green eyes shooting sparks, she looked like a dishevelled and thoroughly irritated kitten. 'You can't really expect me to believe that ridiculous story,' he scoffed, giving her anger another nudge.

'I don't care what you believe!' Sam practically shouted as she struggled out of the depths of the broad couch. 'And I will not stay here to be insulted!'

She got halfway to the door before her feet suddenly left the ground, as Simon swung her up into his arms and carried her back to dump her on the couch. Sam's first reaction was amazement that the top of her dress had stayed in place; her second was to start to get up again. But Simon had other ideas. Sitting down on the edge of the couch, he put one hand on either side of her, effectively blocking her in.

'Now, now, Samantha,' he taunted, 'you're supposed to sit quietly for a while, remember?'

Trying to sit up would just give him another chance to flex his muscles, so she tried a verbal attack instead. 'This whole situation is as much your fault as mine,' she accused.

'The eternal feminine cry: "It's all your fault!"' he mimicked.

'Oh, no,' she denied vehemently. 'You men have first claim on that one—going back to Adam insisting that it was Eve's fault he ate the apple! In any case,' she hurried on before he could reply, 'if you hadn't been imitating a boa constrictor out there, I could have got the misunderstanding cleared up right away. And besides that, why didn't you deny the engagement yourself?'

'Nothing would have given me more pleasure, if Gran hadn't come up in time to hear Mrs Bates broadcasting the news of our imminent wedding. Unfortunately, Gran has her heart set on my getting married, and she looked so pleased and excited that I was afraid of the effect on her if I denied the engagement, especially on top of the strain of the party,' he said a trifle grimly. 'Your fainting just added more excitement and eliminated any chance I might have had to take her aside and break the truth to her calmly and gently.'

'Oh ... well, I see your problem,' Sam admitted. 'But how do we go about explaining to all those people out there that there's been a slight mistake?'

Simon sat back and gave her his wolfish grin. 'We don't.'

Sam stared at him in shocked amazement and wondered if he, like Mr Marlowe, had been at the Planter's Punch. 'Simon,' she began carefully after a moment, 'everyone thinks we're engaged, as in "going to be married".'

He nodded. 'And if we tell them now that

we're not, we'll both look like fools. You may not mind that, but someone in my position can't afford to look foolish or in any way undependable. It makes people who do business with you nervous.'

While he had been speaking, Sam had cautiously edged her way into a sitting position against the arm of the couch. Now that she was looking at Simon, instead of up at him, she felt confident enough to venture some sarcasm. 'So, what do you have in mind? Or are you planning to marry me to reassure your customers?'

'I'm suggesting what you might call a limited engagement,' he replied, ignoring the sarcasm. 'Unless you have a better solution.'

'We could tell them what really happened,' she offered without much hope.

'You mean that crazy story you told me?' he asked mockingly. 'Who would believe it, especially since we didn't deny that we're engaged right away?'

Sam bristled. 'That story may be crazy, but it's also the truth!'

He shrugged. 'Even if it is, would you like to go out there and try to convince that crowd?'

Little though she wanted to, Sam had to admit that he had a point. She also had to admit that she wasn't that keen on looking like a fool herself. What was more, she was at least partially responsible for the misunderstanding with her ploy to help Richard and Amanda.

Ignoring the small, but shrill, voice which warned that she would regret this, she asked, 'How long would you expect this fake engagement to last?'

'Oh, a couple of months or so,' came the careless reply.

'Months?' she almost shrieked. 'Simon, that's impossible!'

'And it won't be a fake engagement,' he went on, ignoring her reaction. 'It will be quite real—except, of course, that you can rest assured that it won't end in marriage. If you keep thinking of it as fake, then you'll never fool anybody.'

The small voice had now given way to loudly clanging alarm bells. 'Simon, I can't——'

'Oh, yes, you can,' he interrupted firmly, shifting his position a bit.

'I won't——'

'You will, Samantha,' he insisted, shifting position again.

Sam was beginning to get annoyed. He could at least let her finish a sentence before he contradicted her. 'Simon, will you——'

But Simon had changed position one more time, and she was interrupted yet again, this time by firm lips which captured hers with commanding precision. When she would have pulled back, his arms went around her and held her still while he rapidly deepened the kiss. Her hands, which had gone up to push him away, ended up gripping the lapels of his jacket as her head began to spin again. This time, though, the sensation was distinctly pleasurable.

Samantha was aware that she should vigorously resist this blatant attempt to overrule her sense with her senses, and as her arms went around him, she told herself that she would start resisting any minute now. But when his hands began to move up and down her spine, pressing her closer and closer against him, the thought wavered and finally vanished altogether.

When he did eventually end the kiss, she felt bereft and whispered his name in questioning reproach, her hands tugging on his shoulders to urge his mouth back to hers. Nothing could be more important, and she was bewildered when he resisted the pressure. Her lashes fluttered up, and she whispered his name again as she stared into heavy-lidded eyes flaring with gold specks.

'You're a witch,' he muttered. 'You make me forget——' His voice broke off as he lowered his head to nuzzle the sensitive area below her ear until she shivered and moaned. 'You'll help me fool everyone, won't you, Samantha?' he murmured huskily.

A dart of alarm stung her, and she moved restlessly. 'Simon . . .'

'Tell me, sweetheart!' he insisted. His hand caressed her bare shoulder, and his mouth explored her neck, soothing away the alarm.

'Yes,' she whispered, responding more to the note of demand than to the question.

His head came up then, and his eyes glowed with fierce satisfaction. 'I'm going to tame you, little witch,' he told her, his voice now edged with hard certainty. 'You've never wanted a man like this before, have you? And in the end you won't care about anything but me!'

The mists of sensual oblivion shredded abruptly as Sam stiffened in shock. The humiliating realisation that Simon had succeeded in undermining her defences produced a combustible blend of panic and anger that evaporated the remnants. For a few moments she hovered on the verge of eruption, until control clamped down once more as she reminded herself that it was lack of sufficient restraint that had caused her downfall.

She became aware that Simon was observing the outward signs of her struggle with interest and quickly unclenched her jaw and her fists. She also noted a galling look of satisfaction on his dark face, and though she was somewhat mollified to see that his breathing was as disturbed as her own, pride demanded that she attempt to rain on his parade of self-congratulation.

Summoning forth all her reserves, she reached up casually to pat her curls into place and said in an excellent imitation of a careless tone, 'I'm duly impressed by your expertise, Simon, but there's no need to look so smug.'

He stood up and looked down at her, one eyebrow raised. 'You're too severe, sweetheart. I'm certainly pleased that you've agreed to co-operate, but "smug" is an exaggeration.'

'Coerced agreements don't count,' she responded, hanging on to her careless tone by a hair, while pretending not to notice the hand he extended to help her to her feet.

There was a moment of silence, during which Sam managed to free herself from the yielding cushions and stand up. When Simon did respond, his voice had acquired a warning edge.

'Samantha, don't push your luck,' he recommended. 'You got us into this, and you aren't going to back out now, just because the result isn't what you were after.'

'I keep telling you, it was——'

'—an accident,' he broke in to finish for her. 'Even so, nothing would have happened if you hadn't been busy linking our names together.'

Trust Simon to find her weak spot, Sam thought resentfully. The fact remained, however, that he had a point, as she had already admitted to herself. Besides, she certainly did not want him to start 'persuading' her again. Perhaps her safest response would be to agree to this engagement for the moment and consider other options later. And she would tie her agreement to one important ground rule, she decided firmly.

'All right, I'll go along—but only on one condition. This engagement is for public consumption only, Simon Radnor, and I will not stand for your taking advantage!'

He looked down at her fierce expression and firmly raised chin, and one corner of his mouth began to twitch. 'Don't worry, Samantha. I won't do anything you don't want me to,' he assured her smoothly.

Sam eyed him suspiciously. Had he put a slight emphasis on the word 'want'? Still, he had agreed, and she did not intend this farce to last long enough for him to get up to mischief.

'What about your grandmother?' she asked, letting the subject go. 'You are going to tell her the truth, aren't you?'

He nodded. 'I'll see how she's feeling tomorrow and tell her then, if possible.' She relaxed a bit, only to stiffen up again at his next words. 'By the way, if anyone asks, you'll be getting your ring this coming week.'

'A ring? Simon, that's carrying things too far!'

'Props are important, Samantha. Wearing a

ring will help you to feel engaged,' he answered adamantly. 'And you can keep it as a memento when this is over.'

'Oh, all right, I'll wear the wretched ring. But you'd better get one you can return, because I'm certainly not going to keep it,' she stated coldly. Did he think he could bribe her with the promise of a piece of jewellery? Well, she would take great pleasure in proving that not all women were weak, greedy creatures by tossing the ring in his cynical face in the not-too-distant future, Sam decided with great satisfaction.

Simon was also feeling satisfied. She had taken his suggestion that she keep the ring as an insult, confirming his opinion that she was not greedy in the ordinary sense. However, nothing showed on his face as he replied. 'Suit yourself. And now, it's time we got back to my guests. I'm sure they're all anxious to offer congratulations,' he ended sardonically.

Sam's satisfaction changed to apprehension as she pictured two hundred guests waiting to descend upon them. 'I need to straighten up first,' she said hurriedly. 'I'll meet you in the hall in a few minutes.'

He raised no objection and even directed her to a back staircase, so that she could avoid the front of the house. To her relief the guest bedroom was empty, giving her a few minutes alone to gather her forces before she began her new role as Simon's fiancée.

'How did I get myself into such a mess?' she muttered out loud as she tugged a comb through her curls. Her sane, sensible life was in tatters and shreds, and all she seemed capable of doing was to apply a makeshift patch here and there. Every time she tried to come to grips—no, that was an unfortunate choice of words—to *deal* with the central problem—Simon Radnor—she ended up worse off than ever.

Sam put down the comb and eyed herself gloomily in the mirror. Sometimes she felt that she hardly knew herself any more; emotion and impulse seemed to guide her actions as often as reason. Look at the way she had reacted to what any sane person would consider a dangerous threat to her future peace. Had she calmly and categorically refused to go along with this engagement? No, she had waffled and wavered and allowed him to manipulate her into agreeing.

A tide of colour spread upward from the top of her dress at the memory of one of his methods of manipulation. How could she have responded to his kiss after he had humiliated her by accusing her of dressing indecently, and then topped the performance by believing that she had tried to trick him into marriage because of his money? Whenever he touched her, she acted like a mindless idiot.

Sam sighed and made a face. She had come up here to prepare herself for facing the multitudes, not to meditate on depressing topics. Anyway, if all else failed, she could always borrow Kate's spear and hold off the Baron with that.

Coming down the front stairs a few minutes later, Sam didn't see Simon, but the owner of the spear was there with John. 'Here she is now,' John said cheerfully. 'Hi, Sammy.'

Kate swung around. 'Aha!' she announced as she sighted her prey. And before Sam had a

chance to say anything, Kate had taken her arm
and was hustling her into the dining-room, which
was presently free of sightseers.

'What's all this talk about you being engaged to
Simon Radnor?' demanded Kate as they seated
themselves at the far end of the table. 'I haven't
even met the man yet, except for a how-do-you-
do as we whizzed by in the receiving line!'

Sam and John looked at each other. 'My real
mother was never this bad,' Sam remarked
solemnly.

'I keep telling her that she needs to have
children,' John replied. 'Then she would be too
busy to harass her friends.'

'But not too busy to harass their father,'
warned Kate with a ferocious scowl.

John leaned back and clasped his hands behind
his neck, putting the seams of his jacket sleeves
under a visible strain as his biceps swelled. 'I'm
willing to risk it,' he told Kate teasingly.

'Stop showing off,' she ordered. 'I'm not
ready for marriage, and two engagements are
enough for one party, even if one is only a
rumour.'

Sam was smiling as she listened to the latest
instalment of a familiar running argument. Kate
had always declared that she would never marry
until she was at least thirty, and John had been
trying for several months now to alter her
timetable.

'Have you really got engaged to my esteemed
boss?' he asked, signalling the end of this round.

Sam found herself in a quandary. Telling Kate
the truth was one thing, but John worked for
Simon, and she didn't want to put him in a

difficult position. 'I suppose so,' she answered brightly.

'Maybe we ought to get Simon's opinion,' John suggested to Kate. 'Sammy doesn't seem too certain about it.'

'He's getting the ring this week,' elaborated Sam, still trying to avoid an outright lie.

'I get it,' said John with a grin. 'It's a unilateral engagement. Simon declared it, and Sam is still trying to figure out what happened. Now, there's a man who knows how to get things done!'

Kate, who had been trying to get a word in, frowned him down. 'How and why?' she asked succinctly.

Sam was still fumbling for an answer when a footstep caused all three to look around. It was Simon, and Sam gave him such a welcoming smile that his eyebrows went up.

'There you are, sweetheart,' he said calmly. 'I wondered where you'd got to.'

Then John was getting up to offer his congratulations. 'You met Kate earlier,' he reminded Simon after shaking his hand.

'Briefly,' Simon agreed, sitting down beside Sam. 'I've heard a lot about you from Samantha.'

'Sam has talked about you, too,' returned Kate, eyeing him thoughtfully. 'But I must say, I was surprised to learn that you two are engaged.'

Simon leaned back and smiled blandly. 'Samantha swept me off my feet,' he replied to Sam's indignation and John's amusement.

'Well, Sam is certainly old enough to make her own decisions, but I wouldn't want you to think she's alone in the world, just because she has no close relatives,' Kate told him, showing her teeth in a smile.

'How fortunate that I hadn't planned to beat her more than once a week, then,' Simon answered in a pleasant voice that fooled nobody.

Sam was beginning to wonder if she was about to witness a battle of the Titans, but John looked unperturbed, so she gave up the idea of trying to intervene. It was a fairly tentative idea, anyway; this evening had already been enough of a trial to her nervous system.

As it happened, Kate was apparently satisfied that she had made her point and greeted Simon's response with her Cheshire Cat grin. And Sam breathed a sigh of relief as his mouth relaxed into an answering smile.

'"Women and rugs are both the better for a good beating",' John intoned piously as the tension faded.

Simon gave a crack of laughter.

'I told you it was a mistake to get him that *Manual For Male Chauvinists* for Christmas,' Kate reminded Sam in long-suffering tones.

'Personally, I think it's pretty low to turn a person's own gift against her,' Sam replied darkly.

John winked at Simon. 'It's only fair to warn you that any man who attempts to assert his natural male superiority with one of these two had better keep a weather eye out for the other, or he's likely to get blind-sided.'

Kate and Sam looked smugly demure.

'You seem to have survived all right,' Simon commented with a smile.

'Tact and diplomacy,' John told him gravely. 'Plus a lot of bobbing and weaving.'

'I'll keep that in mind,' nodded Simon. 'And I'm afraid it's time for Samantha and me to practise some tact and diplomacy among my guests.'

'I'd rather practise bobbing and weaving among them,' said Sam with a grimace as she got up.

'All you have to do is blush a lot and smile shyly,' John told her. 'Let your lord and master do all the talking.'

Sam stared at him balefully before turning to Kate. 'What brought this on?'

'Planter's Punch,' Kate answered, not greatly to Sam's surprise . . . that punch already had a lot to answer for. 'Never mind, though. We'll go over to his place tomorrow morning and enjoy his hangover.'

'Business before pleasure,' Simon reminded Sam, tucking her arm in his. 'We'll see you two later.'

During their absence the living-room had become crowded with people who wanted to be among the first to congratulate the newly engaged couple. If Simon had not linked his arm so firmly with hers, Sam might have broken and fled as her appalled gaze took in the sea of faces that turned towards them as they entered the room.

'Chin up,' murmured Simon when he felt her tense.

Sam gave him a wavering smile. Suddenly he had changed from the bane of her existence into a source of comforting strength, and she clung to him closely as she turned her smile on to the approaching guests. Later she would be wryly amused to remember that for the most part she had followed John's advice, letting Simon do most of the talking as they moved slowly through the living-room and out on to the terrace.

Once the initial flood of congratulations subsided, however, she relaxed. Since their conversation with Kate and John, Simon had been at his most charming, and though Sam wasn't certain why, at least his attitude enabled her to push his angry accusation to the back of her mind for the moment. The sincere best wishes of old friends reminded her uncomfortably that they were deceiving everyone, but no normal person could fail to get some harmless pleasure from the envious looks directed at her by other women. If Simon noticed, he probably attributed the envy to his money, but Sam knew better. His fortune was just a nice extra; few women would look at Simon and think of money first. And if she had to suffer the ill-effects of his undeniable attraction, then she might as well collect a few benefits from it while she had the opportunity.

'You're looking pleased with yourself,' remarked Simon, watching her with a lazy smile as he leaned against the terrace balustrade. For the moment they were alone, with no one close enough to overhear their conversation if they kept their voices down.

'I'm just happy that the worst is over,' she replied. Then a duet of familiar voices caught her attention, and she added ruefully, 'I may have rejoiced too soon. I believe I hear the sound of the Bs approaching.'

He glanced behind her and nodded, then raised a questioning eyebrow. 'Shall we go hide in the garden?'

'Sorry, but I was told not to stray out of the lighted area,' she answered, her dimples giving her away as she tried to look prim.

Simon's eyes went past her again, then returned, glinting with mischief. 'I'm pleased to see that you've learned to follow orders,' he said provocatively, just as they were hailed by Mrs Bates' fluting tones.

CHAPTER SIX

REMEMBERING that conversation late the next morning, Sam had to smile. He had timed his response beautifully, leaving her no chance for a comeback before the Bs were upon them. She sighed and settled herself more comfortably against the trunk of the old oak in her garden. She never knew what to expect next from Simon. Just when she had braced herself to resist the Baron's aggression, he turned into an entertaining, enjoyable companion. Then he caught her off guard again with an outraged objection to a perfectly decent dress.

In fact, now that she considered the matter more calmly, he had sounded jealous, Sam realised. If so, she could stop feeling hurt and concentrate on feeling nervous instead; jealousy was an indication that his pursuit was more than an idle amusement to occupy some free time. Perhaps she should even be grateful that he had decided she was after his money. Surely that would cool his ardour, though with Simon you could never be certain. And why should she care what he thought of her? she asked herself, ignoring the pang of hurt regret which suggested that she did care. If he had a nasty, suspicious mind, that was his problem.

Sam frowned up at the leaves rustling above her. Still, she couldn't help wondering what had made him so cynical about women. More than ever she was convinced that she didn't know the whole story. And though knowing the cause wouldn't change anything, now that she was personally affected, her curiosity had increased. No one had ever doubted her word before, and she had not enjoyed the experience.

The frown changed to a rueful look as she remembered Kate's reaction when she had unburdened herself after early service this morning.

'I don't blame you for being upset,' Kate had sympathised, 'but I doubt that Simon really believes you're as greedy and scheming as all that. If he did, he wouldn't have been so nice after your showdown.'

'Hah! He just got over the worst of his anger by bullying me,' she had retorted, 'and getting his own way put him in a good mood.'

'Well, he must be blind, then. Anyone with blonde curls and Shirley Temple dimples is obviously honest, open, and pure of heart.'

Kate was always so helpful, Sam thought, making a face at a squirrel who was peering down from a branch above her head and energetically telling her off for trespassing. 'Oh, stop scolding! I have a perfect right to be here, and I'm tired of being picked on,' she grumbled.

The squirrel stopped chattering and drew back, regarding her nervously, before resuming its tirade at an increased volume.

'All right, all right—I'll go inside,' she told the irate animal with a sigh.

Seated at the kitchen table with a cup of coffee a few minutes later, Sam started to laugh. Last night Simon had been bossing her around, and now she had been chased out of her own garden by an angry squirrel! She just went from strength to strength! Any time now a pugnacious ant would probably crawl up on to the table and order her out of the kitchen.

Actually, she hadn't felt in control of her life since she had got mixed up in Richard's love affairs, and that wasn't a laughing matter. Still, when she remembered how happy Richard and Amanda had looked last night after the fuss had died down, she couldn't regret her involvement. And how fortunate that they had been too taken up with their new-found bliss to question why Sam wanted to keep the truth about her relationship with Richard from Simon, though Richard had recommended that she not wait too long to explain.

Good advice normally, Sam admitted now, but her situation was hardly normal. Somehow, she didn't think that Simon would find the deception amusing. More likely he would take it as added proof of her scheming, untrustworthy character.

Drat the man, anyway! she thought, blinking away a sudden spurt of tears. Why did he have to come along and upset everything? Maybe she had been in a rut, but it had been a nice, peaceful rut. Sam sniffed dolefully. And now that she was being tugged out of it, she wasn't coping well at all. She had planned to spend this morning figuring out how to extract herself from this 'limited engagement', but her mind kept wandering off on side issues. Anyone would think she didn't really want to get out of this mess. Which was ridiculous, of course. Admittedly she felt more . . . alive when she was with Simon; but living dangerously was reputed to have that effect, and Simon was usually good for a few spurts of adrenalin.

Dismissing these odd thoughts with a shrug, Sam decided to bury herself in the Sunday papers for a while. Maybe later on her mind would be more co-operative.

A couple of hours later Sam was frowning over the crossword puzzle when the phone rang.

'Samantha, are you free this evening?' came the abrupt response to her hello.

Sam was sorely tempted to enquire who was calling, but she opted instead for an even more abrupt reply,

'Why?'

'Gran didn't get up this morning. She insists that she's just resting after all the excitement, but I didn't explain about the engagement in the circumstances,' he answered in a clipped tone. 'She'd like to talk to you since she didn't get much chance to last night, and naturally she assumed that we would be spend the evening together.'

Sam's heart sank, but she couldn't refuse. 'Yes, I'm free.'

'Good. Would you mind driving yourself out here? Sunday is one of Mrs Gessner's days off, and I don't want to leave Gran alone.'

'I don't mind at all,' Sam replied truthfully. She was more than happy to have her own car on hand as a ready means of escape.

'Fine. Then come around six-thirty. You can talk to Gran, and then we'll have dinner,' he told her, then ended the call as abruptly as he had begun.

It was six-thirty on the dot when Sam stepped out of her car in front of the big stone house. She looked cool and neat in a white blouse and Madras plaid skirt, but inside she was worried about how Simon would act, and even more about the coming talk with his grandmother. Not only did she feel guilty about deceiving Mrs Radnor, but she had never been a very convincing liar.

As she reached the door, Simon opened it, looking relaxed and immaculate as always in well-tailored tan slacks and a light-blue silk shirt with the neck open and the cuffs turned up. Also as disturbing as always, Sam admitted, conscious of a fluttery feeling in her middle.

'I thought I heard your car,' he said, standing back to let her in. His smile reassured her on one count, but he proceeded to increase her agitation on the other. 'Gran just finished dinner, and she's waiting for you. She wants to see you alone first, so I'll show you the way in a minute.'

'Alone?' Sam echoed hollowly. 'Simon, can't you stay? What if she asks questions? What if I'm not convincing enough?'

Simon looked amused. 'Samantha, you'll do fine,' he insisted, putting his hands on her shoulders. 'Gran isn't going to conduct an inquisition. And you don't have to convince her, she's already convinced.'

Some of his confidence seemed to flow into her along with the warmth of his hands, and she relaxed with an audible sigh. For all his faults Simon could be amazingly comforting and reassuring when he wished, she reflected. She had no more than completed this thought,

however, when a gleam that had nothing to do
with comfort entered his eyes.

'I'd say that the one who needs convincing is
you,' he told her. 'I don't think you fully realise
yet that you are, in fact, engaged to me. But we'll
work on that, starting with a proper hello.'

Sam, being no fool, had started to pull back
before he had finished speaking—or rather, had
started to try to pull back. It was lowering to
consider that Simon didn't even have to tighten
his gentle hold on her shoulders in order to keep
her in place.

'Simon, don't!' she protested as he gathered
her closer. But he paid no attention, except to
take advantage of her conveniently parted lips.

She tried hard to remain stiff and unresponsive,
but the movement of his lips on hers was starting
that peculiar melting sensation inside her. Soon
her own lips softened, and her hands crept up to
his shoulders and around his neck.

When he raised his head, Simon eyed her
flushed cheeks and glowing eyes and gave a
satisfied nod. 'There, that's better. Now you look
as if you'd just greeted your fiancé.'

This time when she pulled back, he let her go.
Retreating to a safe distance, she drew herself up
and tried a quelling stare. 'Would you please
show me the way to your grandmother's room?'

He was not noticeably quelled, but he did nod
and gesture her towards the stairs. 'If you keep
your nose that high in the air, you're going to trip
going up the steps,' he murmured as she stalked
off.

Sam ignored him.

At the top of the staircase he crossed the hall to

a door which stood partly open and knocked lightly before ushering her into a large, rectangular room with pale cream carpeting and wallpaper patterned in tiny flowers. The front half of the room was a sitting area, with a loveseat upholstered in dusty rose and two matching chairs arranged around a fireplace. The back half was taken up by a walnut bedroom suite, including the fourposter bed in which Mrs Radnor was sitting, propped up by several pillows.

As Sam glanced around, she realised that most of the furniture reflected the tastes of fifty or sixty years ago. 'You brought your home with you,' she said after greeting Mrs Radnor, indicating the furniture with a smile.

Mrs Radnor nodded. 'I've had some of these pieces since I was first married. It wouldn't seem like home without them.' She waved towards a chair pulled up beside the bed. 'Sit down, Sam. Simon, I'll send her downstairs for dinner in fifteen minutes or so.'

Simon accepted his dismissal with a nod, and Sam was left nervously facing his grandmother on her own.

'I must say, I think that shade of lipstick looks better on you than it does on my grandson,' Mrs Radnor remarked. 'No need to blush, my dear,' she added with a smile, 'though it's very becoming.'

'I . . .'

'But you're not looking so nervous and uncomfortable because of my teasing,' Mrs Radnor stated shrewdly as Sam searched for something to say. 'Everything has been happening too quickly, hasn't it? And now you're having doubts, but don't want to upset me by saying so.'

'Well . . .'

'I think you would make Simon an excellent wife, and that he would make you an excellent husband. But you have to feel sure of that yourself,' the old lady went on calmly. 'In the meantime there's no reason for you to feel uncomfortable with me. I don't intend to badger you, and I would miss our talks.'

'Thank you,' Sam managed to reply, trying not to sigh with relief. Mrs Radnor thought she was suffering from bridal nerves!

'But having said that, I do think I should explain something about Simon that will help you to understand him better. I would hope that eventually he will tell you himself, but in my opinion you need to know now, not some time in the future.'

Sam was aware that she had no business listening to confidences offered to her as Simon's supposed future bride, but she kept quiet, her curiosity stronger than her scruples.

'When Simon was twelve,' Mrs Radnor began, 'his mother left his father for another man—an old boy-friend who had become very wealthy. And several months later David, Simon's father, was drowned when he was out sailing and his boat was hit by a sudden squall. To make matters worse, there was gossip about suicide, even though his death was clearly an accident.'

Sam was appalled. 'Poor Simon!'

'After his father's death Alice, his mother, wanted him to live with her and her new husband. But Simon didn't want to have anything to do with her, and we finally persuaded her to leave him with us.' Mrs Radnor shook her head sadly. 'Alice wasn't a wicked person, just shallow and always wanting pretty things and excitement. David had opened his own electrical repair shop and was working long hours to get it going. When this old flame appeared on the scene and started promising her the moon, Alice was already bored and restless and made an easy target.'

'And to Simon she had deserted his father and him for money,' Sam stated, her heart aching for the twelve-year-old boy whose world had fallen apart.

'Yes, and in his mind the desertion was connected with his father's death,' said Mrs Radnor. 'I felt rather sorry for Alice, you know. She was a good mother in her own way, and she did love Simon. I don't believe she realised until too late that she might lose him by leaving. As he grew older, he stopped hating her, but he never let her get close to him again.'

'Is she still alive?'

'No, she died several years ago after a stroke.'

Sam sighed and shook her head. 'No wonder he's so cynical about women!'

'It was bound to affect him,' Mrs Radnor agreed, 'but I don't think the effect would have been so great if it hadn't been reinforced later on. He was only twenty-three when the company began booming, you see. Women started chasing after him, and he discovered that a lot of others welcomed any sign of interest. Even his best friend's fiancée started making up to him.'

'Oh, dear! And he concluded that all women are after money.'

'Most, at any rate,' his grandmother amended pointedly, giving her a smile. Sam blushed and started to feel guilty again. Mrs Radnor continued.

'Of course, after his mother's behaviour he was easier to convince than most. And once you start looking for evidence of greed and weakness, there's always plenty to be found, human nature being what it is.'

'Oh, dear,' Sam said again, wondering now why Simon hadn't strangled her the night before.

'You mustn't brood about it,' Mrs Radnor admonished. 'I just wanted you to know the reason why he can be so unreasonable and suspicious at times. And naturally, this conversation is just between the two of us.'

'Absolutely,' Sam agreed fervently. She didn't care to imagine how Simon would react if he found out that his grandmother had been confiding in her.

When she left Mrs Radnor a short time later, Sam purposely lingered on her way downstairs, trying to get her thoughts in order before facing Simon. Now that she had the whole story, she could certainly understand why he had a poor opinion of women—and why he was unusually close to his grandmother. Sam's own loss had been agonising, but at least she had been old enough to be on her own and had been able to remember both her parents with love and respect.

This morning she had thought that knowing why Simon was cynical wouldn't change anything, but now she discovered that it did make a difference. He seemed more human, more vulnerable, to her now; and even if the circumstances were quite different, they still had in common the tragedy of losing their parents.

It wouldn't do to get carried away with this new view of him, though, she cautioned herself. Simon was no longer a twelve-year-old boy badly in need of comforting. He was a full-grown, dangerously attractive man, whose idea of comforting would be quite different from her own. Besides, she might be able to forgive him now for thinking the worst of her, but she mustn't forget that he still thought it.

Which brought up the question of why he was being so nice ... well, nice in his own baronish way. She would like to think that Kate was right, and he didn't think she was entirely black-hearted, but more likely he was up to something, such as seduction. If so, he was in for a disappointment; however, since she was stuck with this engagement for the moment, she might as well play along. Certainly a charming Simon was preferable to an angry one, she decided with a reminiscent shiver.

Having arrived at this conclusion, she began looking through the downstairs rooms for him. She found him sitting at the kitchen table with a drink and a magazine.

'You're just in time for a drink before we eat,' he said, getting up as he saw her standing in the doorway.

Sam sniffed the air. Several appetising odours were emanating from the direction of the large double ovens. 'You're cooking dinner?' she asked increduously.

'Why not?' he asked, raising one eyebrow haughtily.

'Well ... no reason, I suppose,' she said doubtfully. 'I know a lot of men like to cook ...' She tested the air again and realised that the odours were familiar. 'You're reheating leftovers from the party!'

'What a nose,' he said admiringly. 'Just like Sam.'

She was confused for a moment before she remembered. 'Ah, yes, your beagle.'

'Maybe you and Sam have more in common than I'd realised,' he mused thoughtfully.

'But I thought you said he was devoted and obedient,' she objected innocently.

He just looked at her, his eyes glinting as his mouth slowly curved into a smile. Just wait, his expression said, as clearly as if he had spoken. Before he finally did speak, his smile had changed to a grin after watching Sam glare and blush at the same time.

'Sit down, Samantha. I'll get you a drink.'

Maybe a charming Simon wasn't so preferable, after all, she thought in irritation as he left the kitchen, and she subsided into a chair. Just once she would like to get the better of him.

Simon returned all too soon and put down a glass of sherry in front of her. 'I thought we would eat in here, if you have no objection,' he said as he sat down again opposite her.

'That's fine,' she replied, her manner polite but distant.

'Of course, I can set a place for you in the dining-room, if you would prefer,' he continued.

Sam tried to maintain her distant manner, but the picture of herself eating in lonely splendour in the dining-room while her host ate in the kitchen was too much for her. 'That's a bit far to pass the salt,' she said, the corners of her mouth twitching.

Simon grinned. 'Good. I was looking forward to company at dinner.'

'As a reward for slaving over the hot stove?' she enquired.

'Just for that, I will cook you dinner some time.'

'Let me guess—steak and baked potatoes,' she teased.

He shook his head. 'I learned to cook on a budget. My company dish is spaghetti.'

'That doesn't count as cooking unless you make the sauce from scratch.'

'How else?' he replied in pretended surprise. 'As a matter of fact, I have an authentic old Italian recipe.'

'I'm impressed,' she assured him. 'Where did you get it?'

'From an authentic old Italian,' he said blandly.

Sam groaned. 'I don't believe I walked right into that!'

He laughed and stood up. 'As a forfeit, you can set the table while I collect the food.'

While they ate, Simon refrained from baiting her, and the conversation flowed easily, ranging from the less controversial aspects of last night's party, to Simon's work (which Sam found fascinating, if somewhat incomprehensible), to a comparison of growing up in the city and a small town. It wasn't until they had cleared the table and sat down again with coffee that Sam realised he hadn't asked her about her talk with his grandmother.

'You would have told me if anything terrible had happened,' he shrugged when she mentioned it.

'She saw right away that something was wrong,' she said, her tone faintly accusatory as she remembered his assuring her that there was nothing to worry about.

He gave her a faint smile. 'And?'

'And she decided it was bridal nerves,' she told him.

He leaned back in his chair and eyed her thoughtfully. 'It really bothers you to play a part with Gran, doesn't it?'

'Of course it does! I'm fond of your grandmother, and I don't like fooling her, especially about something that means a lot to her.'

She half expected him to make some sarcastic comment, but he merely nodded and said, 'I don't enjoy it, either, and I'll tell her the truth as soon as I think it's safe.'

After they had finished their coffee, they went upstairs to visit with Mrs Radnor, who was wide awake and pleased to have company. When they finally left her around ten o'clock, Sam announced that it was time she was getting home. And if Simon was aware that she was wary of being alone with him when he didn't have a meal to occupy him, he refrained from saying so and escorted her politely to her car. He did insist on kissing her good night, but he ended it before her knees gave way completely and was decent enough not to laugh when he had to remind her to put on the car's headlights.

On Monday afternoon Simon called the office to report that his grandmother had stayed in bed again that day. Richard suggested that he stop by to see her that evening; however, when Sam talked to Simon afterwards, he reported that Richard had found nothing wrong.

'He thinks the excitement of moving and settling into a new home may finally be catching up to her,' he explained. 'She's not having any pain, and since she's already scheduled to go into the hospital on Sunday evening for her annual physical, he suggested that we just keep an eye on her and let her rest as much as she wants until then.'

'Well, Richard is an excellent doctor, and he does have special training in cardiology,' Sam said reassuringly.

'Then we'll have to pay attention to his prescription for peace and quiet, with no upsets or excitement, won't we?' he replied in a dry tone.

'Oh,' Sam replied in a small voice, having no trouble interpreting that statement. The status would have to remain quo for at least a week.

'Cheer up. At least I saved you from spending your day off here.'

'Why should I spend it there, and how have you saved me?' she asked suspiciously.

'Gran was going to invite you over to use the pool and have lunch with her, but I told her we'd talked about visiting Old Sturbridge Village, and she insisted we should feel free to go on Wednesday.'

Sam was torn between relief, and annoyance at his high-handedness. 'What if I already have other plans?'

'Don't be difficult, Samantha,' he responded

tolerantly. 'From the way you phrased that, you obviously don't, and you did tell me last night that I ought to see Old Sturbridge.'

Old Sturbridge Village in neighbouring Massachusetts was a reconstruction of an American village from between 1790 and 1840. It had been one of Sam's favourite places since she was a child, and she had, indeed, described its attractions with great enthusiasm the night before.

'Well, actually I haven't been up there in several years myself, and you really should see it,' she admitted. Until she got out of this 'engagement', she was going to have to spend some time with Simon, and a trip to such a public place seemed a safe way to accomplish that, she told herself.

'I'll take that as an acceptance,' said Simon, sounding amused. 'I'll pick you up a little before nine.'

When he arrived on Wednesday morning, Sam was ready and waiting. She had awakened early that morning, feeling the excitement of a child promised a special treat. Maybe she couldn't trust Simon further than she could throw him, but surely it couldn't hurt to relax and enjoy the day. It wasn't as if she were suggesting that she relax for an evening, she pointed out to the Voice of Caution. The Voice was not amused, but had to admit that she was stuck with the engagement until Mrs Radnor improved, and that a visit to Old Sturbridge seemed harmless enough.

'A punctual woman,' Simon commented in mock amazement when she opened the door in response to his knock.

'Everyone is allowed an occasional lapse,' replied Sam, refusing to rise to the bait.

He grinned, but said nothing more until they were in the car. As he started the engine, he told her casually, 'You'll find your ring in the glove compartment.'

Sam had been hoping he would change his mind about the ring. When she hesitantly retrieved and opened the small embossed leather box, she wished it even more fervently. Inside was a magnificent emerald ring. The stone was a deep, glowing green, and the setting was beautifully wrought gold in a design which reminded her of pictures she had seen of Renaissance jewellery.

'Simon, I can't wear this!' she protested in dismay.

'Strange, I was so sure you would like it.'

'Of course I like it, it's exquisite,' she returned impatiently. 'Too exquisite to be used as a . . . a prop! And much too extravagant.'

'Now, how do you think everyone, including Gran, would react if I gave you a cheap, ordinary ring?' he asked reasonably.

'But what if something happens to it?'

'It's well insured. Anyway, it's yours, not a loan you need to feel responsible for, if that's what's worrying you,' he added a bit impatiently.

Sam's chin went up. 'I already told you that I would only accept a ring on condition that you take it back later. The ring is supposed to be returned when an engagement ends, you know,' she pointed out sarcastically. 'And you keep insisting that this is a real engagement.'

'Fine, but I won't hold you to that. I imagine

that particular rule is honoured more in the breach than the observance, and you might change your mind.'

His mouth was twisted into the nasty, cynical smile that Sam hated, and she glared at him silently, wishing she could tell him to take his ring and his insulting attitude, and go and sneer at someone else.

'Stop scowling, Samantha, you look like a bad-tempered cherub,' Simon told her, his expression suddenly relaxing.

That remark hit a sensitive spot, and her eyes sparked indignantly. 'I do not appreciate being made fun of,' she announced stiffly, before ruining the effect by continuing, 'It's bad enough having to go through life with dimples and curls without having people making cracks about cherubs!'

'I can see that it would be a trial,' he conceded after a moment with only a slight tremor in his voice. 'My apologies, Samantha, I won't call you a cherub again.'

'I suppose it's silly to get upset,' she admitted, mollified by the apology, 'but if it isn't cherubs, it's Shirley Temple, and——'

Unfortunately, Shirley Temple proved too much for Simon, and the rest of her sentence was drowned in laughter. Sam glared. But the more she glared, the more he laughed, and finally she couldn't help joining in.

When they eventually subsided, he increased speed again, having allowed the car to slow down while his attention was partially distracted from the road. 'It's a good thing we're too late for rush hour. You're a menace to safe driving,' he told her wryly. Then he added casually, 'Better see if the ring fits. I had to guess at the size.'

Sam considered further protest, but she found herself reluctant to disturb the friendly ease that laughter had created between them. In addition, Simon had already knocked down her best objections. She slid the beautiful emerald carefully on to her finger and was not terribly surprised to find that it fitted perfectly. Trust Simon to get it right, she thought ruefully.

'You made a good guess,' she told him, staring down at her hand and watching the stone catch the sunlight. Then she covered it with her other hand, as if she feared being mesmerised by the green fire in its depths.

Simon merely nodded and turned the conversation to less controversial topics as they reached Interstate 84 and headed east towards Hartford, the state capital. At Hartford they picked up I-86 going north to Massachusetts. The sky had been a bit overcast when they had left, but the sun came out as they reached the capital and continued to shine as they approached the border. Soon after crossing the state line, they left the interstate highway, and a short time later Simon pulled into the parking lot at Old Sturbridge Village.

CHAPTER SEVEN

'READY to play tour guide?' he asked as he helped Sam out of the low-slung Porsche.

Sam nodded, her eyes alight with anticipation. 'I already have an itinerary planned out. We'll start with the houses, since they're likely to get crowded first if a lot more people show up this afternoon.'

Simon grinned. '"Lay on, Macduff".'

After paying the admission charge, they walked along a dirt road leading to the Village Green. The parking lot had quickly disappeared in the trees, and only the sounds of insects and human voices disturbed the country quiet. As they came in sight of the Green, a horse and wagon came towards them, driven by a man in early nineteenth-century dress, who smiled and nodded to them as he passed.

'They try to show an operating village here,' Sam explained as she smiled back. 'You often see people doing odd jobs around the buildings and working in the fields and gardens, as well as demonstrating crafts and providing local colour.'

Simon nodded as he looked around the Green. 'You said that these buildings were all brought here from somewhere else, didn't you?'

'All but one or two,' she agreed. 'They were built in various parts of New England, but they all date from the 1700's or first half of the 1800's.'

They were approaching a two-storey, rectangular house with darkly weathered wood siding and small windows. 'This is the Fenno House, the oldest one in the Village,' Sam identified.

'Built in 1704,' added Simon, referring to a pamphlet he had picked up at the entrance. 'Not very cheerful-looking, is it?'

'It's a step up from a log cabin,' Sam replied. 'And people were still thinking about having to defend a house when this one was built. Large windows wouldn't have been much of an asset when Indians were attacking.'

'Except to the Indians, of course,' grinned Simon. 'Actually, this is less like a fort than some. I've seen pictures of houses from this period that were built with the second floor overhanging the first. The overhang had openings in the floor so that the people in the house could fire down on anyone trying to break in the door or windows without exposing themselves.'

'Castle walls had something like that, didn't they?' asked Sam.

Simon gave her an approving nod. 'They did, indeed, and the defenders kept barrels of oil ready to heat and pour on attackers.'

'Yuck!' Sam exclaimed with a shiver.

The interior was definitely spartan to modern eyes, with bare floors, sparse furnishings, and unpadded seating. Only the parlour boasted a rug and a couple of upholstered chairs. And in spite of an outside temperature in the low eighties, Sam was glad that she had brought a light jacket with her. She wondered, as she had on other visits, whether the sturdy wood walls kept heat in during the winter as well as they excluded heat in summer.

As they were looking at a bed with a network of rope instead of springs and a corn husk mattress, Simon turned to Sam and asked, 'Would you like to try changing places with one of your ancestors?'

Sam looked up at him and had a sudden vision of herself in a long dress and white cap, sewing in front of the open fireplace in the big kitchen, while Simon sat opposite in homespun shirt and pants, smoking a long clay pipe. Then the vision disappeared, and she was annoyed to find herself blushing as she focused again on his enquiring gaze.

'I wouldn't mind switching places for a while, just to see what life was really like a couple of hundred years ago. But I wouldn't want to go back for good,' she said, hoping that he hadn't noticed her heightened colour.

'It would be interesting to try it,' he agreed. But as Sam turned to leave the room, he added in a musing tone, 'Now, I wonder why that question made you blush?'

Apparently he did not expect an answer, and Sam didn't surprise him with one.

The Fitch House, built in 1737, was next on her agenda. Although of a different design, it had the same rough exterior and unadorned interior as the Fenno House. However, the Richardson House, dating from 1748, was of salt-box construction, a style often seen in modern housing developments.

'The paint and extra windows make quite a difference, too,' Simon observed as they approached the brick-red clapboard house with its neat white trim.

'It's a lot more comfortable-looking inside, too,' Sam told him, 'though I'd still want to add a few more rugs and cushions if I were going to live here.'

As they walked around, admiring the simple elegance of the painted walls, wainscoting, and more detailed wordwork, Sam reminded Simon that his house had been started around the same time as this one.

He nodded. 'I was just thinking that. But I doubt that the original farmhouse was as fancy as this.'

'If you think this is fancy, wait till you see General Towne's place,' she told him.

The General Salem Towne House, as it was properly known, was sited on the bank of the Village mill pond and dominated one end of the Green. Constructed in 1796, this residence had white clapboard siding, black shutters, and a hip roof. The interior was papered, carpeted, and decorated with carved mouldings, mantels, and waiscoting. The furnishings were equally elaborate. Altogether, the house looked like what it was—the residence of a wealthy eighteenth-century gentleman farmer.

'It is beautiful, but the whole effect is a bit too rich for my blood,' Sam commented thoughtfully as they stood in the drawing-room. 'Or maybe "too stiff" is a better way of putting it. Your living-room is formal, but it's still comfortable. I wouldn't feel as if I were committing sacrilege if I kicked off my shoes and curled up in a chair.'

Simon grinned. 'You're certainly welcome to

curl up in any of my furniture whenever you wish,' he told her, putting a caressing note in his voice that stroked her like a warm breeze.

He obviously intended her to pick up the change from 'chair' to 'furniture', which could include beds, and she answered him in kind. 'Very generous of you,' she said sweetly, 'but I was only speaking hypothetically. I keep both feet on the floor in other people's homes.'

'Touché,' he acknowledged. 'And you didn't even blush!'

'I'm getting hardened,' Sam agreed, her dimples showing. Coming out ahead in one of these little exchanges made a nice change, especially when she had the unfamiliar weight of Simon's ring on her finger to remind her of arguments she had lost.

On one side of the house was a formal garden with brick paths, a small white summerhouse with a charming view of the pond, and a grape arbour arching over one section of pathway. After touring the inside of the house, they strolled outside to admire the display of summer blossoms and the carefully pruned shrubs. When they reached the summerhouse, Sam lingered to enjoy the view and watch the sunlight catch in countless drops of water on the shifting surface of the pond.

'I get hypnotised by water,' she told Simon ruefully.

He smiled and shook his head. 'I'm in no rush.'

Sam nodded, then directed his attention off to the right. 'If you look through the trees, you can see the covered bridge. I always cross it whenever I come to Sturbridge. There was one just like it that we used to drive over on the way to my grandparents' house when I was a child.'

After a quick glance at the bridge, he had returned his attention to Samantha, and the wistful look on her face as she spoke stirred up an urge to protect and comfort her. She was so damned vulnerable in some ways, he thought irritably. And for the first time he wondered what would happen to her when the affair he planned had ended, as all affairs do.

Then the cynicism that was so deeply ingrained in him took control again. As she had once emphatically told him, she had been taking care of herself for years and didn't need his concern. No doubt some other man would soon come along to offer the wedding ring he had no intention of bestowing on her. And by then, the thought of her in another man's arms would no longer seem unendurable, he reminded himself grimly.

'Ready to go?' he asked, a harsh edge to his voice.

Sam turned her head and looked up at him in surprise. 'I was ready five minutes ago,' she said with a frown as a vagrant puff of wind nudged one blonde curl on to her forehead.

'So you were,' he agreed, his mood lightening again. He reached out to brush back the curl, his fingers lingering for a moment. 'But five minutes ago, I hadn't realised that I'm starving. Let's take a break for lunch.'

'Fine with me,' Sam replied absently. From any other man she would have taken that casual gesture as a sign of affection. But Simon was hardly likely to feel any affection for a woman he believed had tried to trick him into marriage, even if he had seemed to have got over his anger quickly enough. Probably affectionate gestures were just part of his repertoire of seduction techniques, she thought, feeling a pang of regret that surprised her.

'We need to go back to the car first,' Simon said as they walked back out to the Green.

'Did you forget something?'

'No, but that's where our lunch is. I had Mrs Gessner pack a basket for us.'

'Well, it's a beautiful day for a picnic, but will I be able to move afterwards?' she questioned, remembering Mrs Gessner's version of afternoon tea.

'I'll stop you before you become immobile,' Simon promised.

After collecting a large wicker picnic basket and a blanket from the trunk of the car, they walked over to the open area set aside for picnickers. One of the wooden tables set out there was free, but when offered a choice, Sam opted for spreading the blanket out under the shade of a tree.

'My mother used to say that sitting at a table was just eating outside, not a real picnic,' she told Simon as she sat down to unpack the basket at his invitation.

'And here comes the other essential ingredient,' he said wryly, brushing away an ant that had already appeared on a reconnaissance mission.

'As long as they stay off the piece of food I'm actually eating, they're welcome to any crumbs,' laughed Sam. 'And how many people did you tell Mrs Gessner would be here, anyway?' she asked

as she finished unpacking cold chicken, sandwiches, hard-boiled eggs, potato salad, macaroni
salad, tossed salad, pickles, rolls, strips of carrot
and celery, cheese and crackers, fruit, pastries,
and a bottle of wine.

'She wanted to be sure there would be
something you like,' Simon answered gravely.

Sam shook her head and laughed. 'Well, what
will you have?'

'Chicken, tossed salad, and a couple of rolls,'
was his modest choice.

'It's a wonder Mrs Gessner doesn't hand in her
resignation,' she teased, handing him the bottle
and a corkscrew.

'I think she regards me as a challenge.'

A woman could be tempted to do that, Sam
thought, watching him covertly as he concentrated on removing the cork. Tempted to think
that she could be the one to break through the
cynicism and mistrust. She, of course, was too
smart to fall into a trap like that.

Simon looked up just then with a smile that lit
up his dark face. 'Glasses?'

Sam's heart gave an odd jolt, and she passed
over the glasses with hands that felt suddenly
shaky. Was she too smart . . . or was she so dumb
that she had fallen into the trap without even
realising it? Was that the real reason she had
agreed to this engagement? Her mind churning,
Sam automatically took the filled glass held out to
her and passed Simon his plate. But that would
mean that she was in love with him—had
probably been falling in love with him for weeks!

'Samantha?'

Sam blinked and brought her eyes back into

focus, to find Simon regarding her with a quizzical smile. 'What would have you been off visiting?' he enquired.

'I . . . I was thinking about what you said earlier—about switching places,' she improvised hastily, and began to fill a plate for herself.

'Unless your ancestors were wealthy enough to keep servants, you'd have a hard time of it,' he observed. 'Housework was hard physical labour in those days, what with hauling around iron cooking pots and washing clothes on a scrubbing board. And the chores were endless. Women needed heft and muscle almost as much as men did for their work.'

Well, Simon certainly could manage all right back then, she thought, eyeing his muscular body as he lay stretched out on the blanket, propped up on one arm. She remembered noticing at the party that not even John's bulk could reduce his aura of power and strength. Her eyes lingered, and her memory shifted to how it felt to be held closely against him. A sudden yearning filled her, shaking her with its intensity, and her mind finally accepted what her body and heart already knew. Against all sense and caution, she had fallen in love with Simon!

'Stop brooding about the past and eat,' suggested Simon, interrupting her thoughts again.

She glanced up and met his amused look with a dazzling smile. By rights she ought to be filled with dismay; instead, she felt almost light-headed from relief at finally admitting the truth and more determined than ever to enjoy today.

'You're right, it's too beautiful a day to brood,'

she agreed, and attacked her lunch with an appetite that had Simon warning her that he did not propose to carry her around the rest of Old Sturbridge because she was too full to walk.

For the rest of the afternoon Sam continued to hold all troublesome thoughts at bay. Her physical awareness of Simon was more acute than ever, but instead of dulling her reactions to the world around her, her awareness seemed to finely tune her senses. The pinks, yellows and reds of flowers blazed more brightly, the scent of new-mown grass drifted lightly in the air, and the heat of the sun was a tangible touch on her skin. Sam couldn't remember feeling this joyously alive since her parents had died, and she revelled in it, hugging the feeling to her like a child.

As she had expected, Simon particularly enjoyed the demonstrations at the blacksmith, tin, cooper, and other craft shops. And if her attention was divided between watching the craftsmen at work and watching him, he didn't appear to notice. From the shops they went on to the grist mill and carding mill, then to the working farm on the outskirts of the village.

Here, Simon surprised her by falling into conversation with one of the staff and asking knowledgeable questions about crops and growing methods.

'A cousin of Gran's used to have a small farm in Pennsylvania, and I worked there summers when I was in high school,' he explained as they walked on past fields where crops grew and ripened, enclosed by split-rail fences.

'Did you like it?' asked Sam, thinking how much she still had to learn about him.

'Yes, I did. It was hard work—backbreaking at times—but very satisfying. And it was a whole new world to learn about for a boy from New York City.'

'Probably kept you out of trouble, too,' she suggested teasingly.

'Not altogether,' he answered, with a certain look in his eye which prompted jealous visions of well-endowed farmers' daughters.

On the way back from the farm, they detoured to cross the covered bridge. It was dim and cool inside, and their footsteps on the wooden planks echoed hollowly from the uncovered rafters of the peaked roof.

'I suppose the idea behind the covering was to protect the bridge from the weather, so that it would last longer,' Simon commented, 'but I imagine a covered bridge also was a convenient stopping place for courting couples.'

Sam grinned. 'The covered bridge near my grandparents' was officially named the Kingston Bridge, but the locals all called it the Kissin' Bridge, so I expect you're right.'

Simon chuckled and came to a halt, drawing her around to face him. 'It's a shame to let good traditions go to waste,' he murmured, hazel eyes dancing.

He was teasing her again, but Sam couldn't respond with the expected protest; yearning for his touch rose up in a great wave and overwhelmed her. As he bent his head, she held her breath, then released it on a shaky sigh as his mouth touched hers. What had started as a teasing gesture quickly turned serious as he responded instinctively to her soft, parted lips.

His arms slid around her and urged her closer, and she came with eager willingness, giving no thought to how he might interpret her response. For the moment nothing mattered but the joy of his touch, and the pleasure of expressing the new-found love which she could not reveal in words.

Her hands were engaged in a fascinating exploration of the contours of his back, when the sound of high young voices penetrated her absorption. Simon pulled his mouth away and muttered something under his breath. His arms tightened for a moment, then reluctantly let her go. Hurriedly smoothing down her clothes as the voices drew nearer, Sam barely heard his murmur of, 'You do pick your times, little cat,' and paid little attention to it. Instead she concentrated on appearing casually at ease as they started walking towards the family group approaching the bridge from the other side.

When they emerged into the bright sunlight again, Simon glanced at his watch. 'It's after four-thirty—getting on for closing time. Shall we head back to the car?' As he spoke, his eyes wandered over her face in a visual caress that threatened to give Sam's returning composure a severe setback.

'All right,' she agreed, concealing her reluctance. She wasn't ready to leave and end this enchanted day, but a few more minutes would not find her any more willing, and she still had the trip home before the day was completely over.

'I'd like to come back again some time,' Simon remarked as they walked to the parking lot, 'and take a closer look at some of the collections and exhibits.'

'There's always more to see,' Sam agreed, pushing away the depressing thought that the next time Simon visited Old Sturbridge, this engagement would probably be long over, and someone else would accompany him. She wasn't going to start brooding now. Plenty of time for that later, she told herself wryly.

On the way home they ran into heavier traffic for the first hour, then stopped for a leisurely dinner, so it was approaching eight-thirty when Simon pulled up in front of Sam's house. An active day—both physically and emotionally—fresh air, and the wine with dinner had left her drowsy, and she gave a gigantic yawn in spite of herself as he turned off the engine.

'I'd say you're due for an early night,' he observed, reaching over to ruffle her curls.

Sam considered objecting to being treated like a little girl but couldn't summon enough energy. Instead she mumbled something about coffee.

He shook his head. 'You'd fall asleep before the coffee was done. Next time, little cat. Speaking of which, I'm flying to Las Vegas tomorrow for a convention. Not a part of business I enjoy, but I have to make an appearance at these things occasionally. At any rate, that means I won't see you again until Sunday.'

Sam started to reply, but was caught by another yawn.

'Never mind, I'll just assume you wanted to say you'll miss me,' he teased, and got out of the car before she could try again.

He walked her to her door, waited while she

opened it, and gave her a slow, lingering kiss that curled her toes and left her trembling. 'Sweet dreams, Samantha,' he murmured before pushing her gently inside and pulling the door closed behind her.

Propped against the hallway wall, she listened to the well-bred rumble of the Porsche start up and then fade away down the street. 'Devil!' she accused, her lips curved in a smile. How was she supposed to go calmly off to sleep after that? And she would miss him, though it was probably just as well that he had to go out of town again. She had some thinking to do, and she was in no state to manage coherent thought tonight.

The next morning Sam woke up early, feeling on top of the world, only to wonder a moment later what she was feeling so good about. Yes, she was in love for the first time in her life; and yes, she felt like a new woman. But what did she imagine the future would hold? For the moment she had the engagement and Simon's own interest to hold him, but how long would either last?

During the day at the office she alternated between blinking back tears as she tried to imagine life without Simon, and staring at the emerald ring with an abstracted smile, dreaming of a happy ending. By the time she got home, she was convinced that the entire situation was hopeless and had decided on names for their first two children.

Fortunately, she found Kate waiting for her with a pitcher of iced tea, a sympathetic ear, and a most unladylike whistle when she was shown the ring.

After listening to Sam unburden herself, she announced, 'First, may I say that I am dee-lighted to hear that that shroud of caution you've been walking around in for years has developed a large tear. I sometimes wondered if I'd ever see the day that you'd take a risk like falling in love.

'Second,' she continued, 'in the inimitable words of some baseball person, it's not over until it's over. Being prepared for the worst is one thing. Convincing yourself that it will happen is quite another.'

'That's all very well, but even if his opinion of me isn't as bad as I first thought, it can't be exactly outstanding, either.'

'Since when did love depend on the virtue of the loved one? Amanda certainly wasn't any prize when Richard fell in love with her. He may have been astute enough to recognise her potential, but he had no guarantee that she would ever fulfil it.'

Sam brightened for a moment, but only for a moment. 'Richard had nothing against falling in love; Simon has a great deal against it.'

'Well, I'm still not convinced that he's a hopeless case, but I suppose you're wise to assume that his intentions are strictly dis-honourable.' Sam nodded glumly. 'So, what are you going to do, if an old friend may ask?'

Sam was silent for a moment before answering, 'I'm stuck with this engagement until we're certain that Mrs Radnor is all right, so I can hardly avoid seeing him. And let's face it, I couldn't bring myself to avoid him, anyway. I want to spend as much time with him as I possibly can.' She sighed and continued rather sadly, 'But as much as I love him, I just couldn't

cope with an affair. I know I'm old-fashioned—
Miss Beasley and I are probably the only virgins
over twenty-one in Westfield—but I don't want
to give myself to someone, even Simon, as a
temporary amusement.'

'I doubt if you and Miss Beasley are entirely
without company,' Kate responded with a smile,
'but that's really beside the point. You should do
what's right for you, and if that makes you old-
fashioned, tough!'

'There is still one problem, though,' Sam
mentioned in a small voice. 'When Simon kisses
me, I tend to forget any resolutions I've made.'

'You mean the noble Baron makes hash of your
noble convictions,' said Kate with a chuckle.
When Sam failed to respond, she coaxed, 'Cheer
up! Maybe he'll wait until you're unengaged
before attacking in force. After all, starting an
affair now could seem risky from his point of
view.'

That effort was more successful, though Kate
would have cheerfully bitten her tongue if she
could have foreseen that she had planted an idea
in Sam's mind which would germinate all too
soon with unfortunate consequences.

Whether due to lingering cautiousness, or a
touch of inherited New England pessimism, Sam
put no faith in Kate's suggestion that Simon
might not be hopeless; but naturally, that didn't
stop her from devoting every free minute during
the next two days to thinking about him. At times
she was still amazed that she loved a man whose
effect on her was so unstable. He could move her
to furious anger, or to a desire that overwhelmed
her; he irritated her and then made her laugh in

spite of herself. He was abrupt, exasperating, and cynical—and her life would seem barren and colourless without him.

When the phone rang on Sunday morning, she jumped up to get it, then forced herself to wait a couple of rings before answering.

'Did you behave yourself while I was gone, Green Eyes?'

'I always behave myself,' she said, firmly controlling a surge of pleasure at the sound of his voice.

When he didn't reply immediately, she suddenly recalled that he believed her behaviour had left something to be desired on at least one occasion and groaned inwardly at her unfortunate response. However, when he did speak, his voice was only mildly sarcastic.

'Life in a small town must be even more restricting than I'd thought!'

'How was your trip?' Sam put in quickly.

'Worthwhile, but mostly boring,' he answered. 'By the way, thank you for calling Gran every day while I was gone.'

'Oh . . . well, I knew she would be missing you,' she said, feeling a bit flustered and guilty because she had made the calls partly on her own account. Given a little encouragement, Mrs Radnor had been happy to devote most of the conversation to talking about Simon, and Sam had collected all sorts of fascinating information, from his grade point average in high school to his favourite foods.

'I'm taking Gran over to the hospital early this evening,' he continued. 'Why don't you come along and help me get her settled, then we'll have dinner afterwards?'

'All right,' she agreed happily, adding, 'Your grandmother doesn't seem too pleased about having her annual physical!'

'She described it this morning as two days of being poked, prodded, and bullied by nurses,' Simon reported wryly. 'I'm hoping your presence will distract her from the impending torture on the way there. We'll pick you up a little before seven, by the way, and dress casually.'

With that last instruction in mind, Sam chose to wear peasant-style slacks and jacket in off-white cotton, with a peach-coloured sleeveless top. In order not to keep Mrs Radnor waiting in the car, she was sitting on her front porch when Simon drove up in a dark blue Cadillac Seville.

He met her part way up the walk and tilted up her chin for a quick, hard kiss. 'You should have waited inside,' he reproved. 'I was looking forward to saying hello in private.'

'You never say hello,' Sam pointed out idiotically, her eyes locked with his, then blushed when he laughed.

'Nice of you to come along,' Mrs Radnor said when Sam was settled in the back seat behind Simon, 'though why I have to be shut up like a prisoner when I'm feeling fine, I'll never understand.'

'The tests are easier to do in the hospital,' Sam reminded her with a smile, 'and having an annual physical is just common sense. Besides, you have been a bit under the weather lately.'

'Oh, I haven't been sick, just taking a little vacation,' Mrs Radnor insisted. 'And I may take another after a couple of days in the hospital!'

'Gran is annoyed because I made her promise not to terrorise the hospital staff,' Simon put in.

'I said I would try,' corrected Mrs Radnor. 'But I don't intend to put up with youngsters sixty years younger than I am calling me by my first name and talking to be as if I were in my second childhood!'

At the hospital, which was located in a town north of Westfield, they accompanied Mrs Radnor to her private room. A large bouquet of bright summer flowers stood on the chest of drawers, and Mrs Radnor looked at them with pleased approval. 'Thank you, Simon. They do cheer the place up,' she told her grandson.

He nodded, then left the room, saying he would be back shortly. Sam stared after him, thinking how very kind and thoughtful he could be. She was unaware how wistful she looked, and how closely Mrs Radnor was observing her.

After a minute the old lady remarked, 'Simon has gone to have a word with the head floor nurse to make sure that I'll be treated with the proper respect. And to tell her to call him if I get difficult.'

Sam started and then laughed when she saw the twinkle in Mrs Radnor's eye. 'You like terrorising everyone, don't you?' she accused.

'When you get to be my age, there aren't many amusements left,' Mrs Radnor said unrepentantly. 'Besides, it's good for people to be reminded that you don't lose your wits with your teeth. And they like it, you know—makes them feel a bit less afraid of growing old themselves.'

Back in the car Sam repeated that conversation to Simon, who laughed and said, 'Gran was right,

I was talking to the head nurse. And she's probably right about the rest, too. I tease her, but the fact is that her former doctor told me she was a great favourite with the staff at the hospital in New York.'

'Where are we having dinner?' Sam asked curiously a little bit later. The route he was taking wasn't an obvious one for any of the local restaurants.

'Home,' he answered briefly.

'I thought your grandmother said that Mrs Gessner left this morning to visit her son for a couple of days,' Sam said in surprise.

'She did. I'm making good on my promise to cook for you.'

Oh, dear, Sam thought. Now what was she going to do? An evening spent secluded with Simon sounded delightful, but also dangerous. Could she take the risk? Then the memory of her conversation with Kate came back, giving her sufficient excuse to decide in favour of her heart rather than her head. After all, if she *was* safe until the engagement was ended, she would certainly come to regret having passed up this opportunity to have Simon to herself.

'You mean I get to sample the authentic old Italian sauce this evening?' she asked out loud.

Simon nodded. 'It's simmering on the stove right now.' He hadn't missed her slight hesitation before answering. After their trip to Old Sturbridge he had believed that she had finally stopped hiding. She had been different that day, more open and responsive than she had ever been before, especially when he had kissed her on the covered bridge. It was unfortunate that he had

had to go away the next day, giving her time for second thoughts; but he knew, all too well, the fierce strength of the hunger they created in each other, and he was certain that no second thoughts could vanquish that need. Soon, now, she would stop struggling against the snare of desire that held them both.

When they reached the house, he drove around the back and took her in through the kitchen door. Once inside, he helped her off with her jacket. His fingers brushed lightly against her as he did so, but he appeared not to notice when she shivered in reaction.

'I'm going to put you to work making the salad while I make the spaghetti,' he said as he removed his own sports jacket and turned up his cuffs. 'Do you want an apron?'

'I won't need one until I start eating the spaghetti,' she answered ruefully. 'I tend to end up speckled with sauce unless I'm careful.'

'And those light-coloured clothes will show every speckle,' he said, shaking his head. 'I should have warned you that we were having Italian food. You'll notice that I took sensible precautions.'

Sam had noticed the colour of his clothes, but her thoughts had been running more to how sexy he looked in the dark brown shirt and slacks than to how suitable the colour was for eating spaghetti. 'I'll just have to eat slowly,' she replied. 'It will give me a chance to savour your fantastic sauce.'

'True,' he agreed, tongue in cheek. 'The salad makings are in the refrigerator. I'll get you a bowl and a knife.'

She was tearing up lettuce when he came up behind her and reached around to put a glass of wine on the counter. 'To stimulate your appetite,' he murmured before moving away again.

Sam frowned at the glass for a second. Then her brow cleared, and she took a sip. No need to get paranoid just because he happened to touch her while he was helping her off with her jacket and made a remark which might be interpreted more than one way. Her own intense consciousness of him was probably making her overreact.

During the meal, though, she continued to be plagued by acute sensitivity to everything about him. His eyes seem to glow with a special warmth when they rested on her—the angle of the light, she told herself. His voice was a rough caress that sent shivers of pleasure through her—a quirk of the room's acoustics, no doubt. And whenever she spoke, he seemed to watch her mouth as if he was imagining it moving against his—her fascinating conversation?

'I can give you ice cream or some of Mrs Gessner's baking for dessert,' Simon said when they both were finished.

She shook her head. 'Neither for me, thank you. All I can manage is coffee.'

By the time the two of them had straightened up the kitchen, the coffee was ready, and Simon suggested that they have it in the sitting-room. Sam had intended to take one of the chairs, but she somehow ended up sitting next to him on the big sofa facing the fireplace. The large stone house stayed cool except during the very hottest weather, and she shivered as she picked up her cup from the tray, finding the room chilly after the kitchen, which had been warmed by the heat from the stove.

Setting her cup down again, she said, 'I think I'll get my jacket.'

'Sit still. I'll light the fire instead,' he told her, gesturing towards the neatly stacked wood in the fireplace.

'A fire in the middle of summer?' she asked doubtfully.

'You can comfort your thrifty New England soul with the thought that the wood was free,' Simon said gravely as he got up. 'We have a couple of cords of deadfalls from the grounds cut up and stacked outside.'

'In that case, I won't say another word,' promised Sam, her dimples showing.

After lighting the fire he went over to a cabinet which contained an elaborate stereo system and started a tape. The beautiful strains of Beethoven's Moonlight Sonata began to drift through the room.

'I love this piece,' Sam remarked, trying to stifle an increasing nervousness. Admittedly Simon now had his hands free, and there was no longer a table between them; but Beethoven was hardly standard seduction music, and Simon wasn't turning off lights or plying her with brandy.

'It's a favourite of mine, too,' he replied, sitting down again and stretching out his legs. Then he turned to look at her, his mouth quirking up. 'Why don't you take off your shoes and put your feet up? You look as if you're about to jump up and dash off somewhere!'

Sam flushed, feeling like a fool as she realised that she was sitting primly erect on the edge of the couch. This was getting ridiculous! Taking a deep breath, she kicked off her sandals and slid back to lean against the corner of the sofa, tucking her legs up beside her and forcing her body to relax.

'That's better,' he approved. He reached over to put his hand on her foot, and the newly relaxed Sam promptly jerked and almost spilled her coffee. 'You feet are like ice,' he frowned, ignoring her reaction. 'I'll get a blanket to throw over your legs.'

'My hands and feet are almost always cold. I'm fine, really,' she insisted, then wished she had let him get the blanket, as he began to gently massage her feet with his big hand, presumably to warm them. So much for relaxing, she thought mournfully.

'"Cold hands, warm heart",' he quoted, with a smile that had the organ in question doing flip-flops in Sam's chest.

'Cold hands, poor circulation,' she returned in a bright voice. Her circulatory system was certainly operating well enough at the moment, though. Judging by how quickly the warmth from his hand was spreading through her, her corpuscles were all galloping madly around at full speed!

Her eyes fastened on to his tanned, muscular hand, which had begun to edge up to her ankle with hypnotic slowness. One part of her mind yelled, 'Stop him!' but the rest was already trapped by unreasoning fascination, like a bird watching a snake. She was dimly aware of the music and the whisper and crackle of the fire, but otherwise her attention was absorbed by Simon's touch and her own reactions to it.

CHAPTER EIGHT

'RELAX, Samantha, you're too tense,' Simon ordered softly. 'Look at the way you jumped just now!'

He must be joking, she thought vaguely as her eyes moved up to a wrist twice the size of her own, and on to a powerful forearm with a light covering of dark hair. How could she relax when every nerve in her body was coiled up like a spring?

So intense was her concentration that she did not even realise he had moved closer until the cushion beneath her started to tilt. He reached out with his free hand for her coffee cup. 'Let me take that before you spill what's left,' he murmured, removing the cup to the safety of the end table.

Sam blinked and raised her eyes to meet his. 'What are you doing?'

'I put your cup down, so you wouldn't spill the rest of the coffee all over us when I kiss you,' he explained patiently, his eyes dancing with laughter and something more.

'Oh, but . . .'

His lips met hers in a slow, gentle kiss. And finally the nervousness which had plagued her all evening began to seep away. So that was why she had been so tense, she thought, pleased to have the matter cleared up. She had just needed to have Simon hold her and kiss her like this. Just a harmless little kiss . . .

He drew back slowly, then stood and picked her up in his arms to move her further down the sofa, where she could lie full length along the cushions. Then he stretched out beside her, his body blocking out the heat from the fire and replacing it with his own warmth. This time his mouth was firmer and demanded more of a response, and she gave it willingly. He would stop soon, Kate had said so, she assured herself, her pleasure-fogged mind turning a suggestion into a certainty.

As he sensed how freely she was responding, Simon hesitated and almost drew back. He suddenly felt like a hunter who had successfully stalked a rare and elusive creature, only to wonder at the moment of success if he had the right to take his prize. Then her hands began to move over him in a light caress, and the moment passed as desire shuddered through him, and his own control began to slip.

Minutes passed, and Samantha was dizzily spinning on a rising spiral of pleasure when she became aware that Simon was undoing the button on her slacks. As her hand moved automatically to stop him, she suddenly realised how deeply aroused he was. Panic flared up to dampen her own desire, and she stiffened when he pushed away her hand and started to pull down the zipper.

'Simon, don't!' she gasped, grabbing his hand again.

'It's all right, little cat,' he whispered huskily. 'Let me love you. I've wanted you for so long.'

'No! Simon, stop—you mustn't!'

When Sam began to struggle, Simon instinctively moved to subdue her before his mind had properly registered that the girl who had been responding with a passion almost equal to his own was suddenly resisting him just as passionately. Even after he had used his greater strength and weight to force her to lie still, he tried to soothe her, until he discovered from her half-frantic protests that she did not intend, and never had intended, to let him make love to her.

Aching with desire, Simon was in no mood to be fair or reasonable. Obsessive need had destroyed his usual ironic detachment, and his distrust of women rose up to sharpen his painful frustration. For a moment he had an urge to take what should be his, ignoring Samantha's protests. The urge passed quickly, but left a desire to punish what he saw as her deceitfulness.

Sam had watched fearfully as anger first drove the colour from his face, then darkened it with a flush of rage. She was painfully aware of her vulnerability as she lay trapped beneath him. Her blouse and bra were lying discarded on the floor, and she herself had removed Simon's shirt, eager to run her fingers through the dark triangle of hair covering his chest, and to feel the smooth skin of his back and shoulders. But now, his naked torso gave him a primitive look that stretched her nerves taut. If he decided to ignore her protests, what chance did she have? she thought despairingly. Her eyes went to his face, then dropped away again. He looked as if he would enjoy hurting her.

'Playing tricks again, Samantha?' he asked savagely, his mouth twisted by an ugly, taunting smile. 'Maybe if I take you now, it would cure you once and for all.' The smile widened as she gasped. 'Were you hoping that I'd offer marriage in order to satisfy the desire you've aroused—or was this supposed to be a punishment because I didn't agree to marry you before?'

'No! You're w-wrong, all wrong,' she stammered. 'You must know that!'

'Why must I?' he snarled. 'You would hardly be the first woman to use sex as a weapon. And you use it very well, you scheming little witch!'

Sam was all too aware that he still wanted her, and her pale face flushed at his words.

He laughed and then bent his head to nip almost painfully at her bare shoulder. 'Shall I change your mind for you, Samantha?' he whispered harshly. 'I know you weren't faking your response. You wanted me, didn't you?'

She forced herself to remain still, but her voice trembled as she said, 'Please don't, Simon.' For a moment she was afraid he was going to ignore her, then he gave an exclamation of disgust and thrust himself away from her.

As he stood, he scooped up her clothes and dropped them over her, before picking up his own shirt. 'Get dressed,' he ordered roughly as he walked away.

Sam complied as quickly as her trembling fingers allowed. Only when her shirt was neatly tucked into her slacks did she look around. Simon had disappeared, and she hesitated for a moment before going out cautiously into the side hall. The sound of water running hard in the powder room told her where he was, and she went hurriedly into the kitchen, hoping that she would have time to relieve the dryness in her throat with a drink of water before he came out.

When he entered the kitchen a couple of minutes later, she was just setting down an empty glass. His hair was damp, and his shirt clung in spots, as if he had doused himself and not dried thoroughly before putting it on again. His mouth curved in a sardonic smile as he noticed that she had her jacket on and buttoned, but he did not comment on her obvious attempt to armour herself in an extra layer of clothing.

'I'm sure you'll understand if I end this delightful evening early and take you home now,' he said silkily.

Same winced at the taunting sarcasm in his voice. She knew that she would do better to keep quiet, but now that she was in no immediate danger, she felt that she had to at least try to explain. 'Simon, I——'

'No, Samantha! If you have any sense, you'll just keep quiet.'

On the way back to town he drove with a carefully controlled ferocity that was almost worse than recklessness. He ignored Sam completely, neither speaking nor looking at her. She sat quietly, her hands clenched in her lap, and tried to stem the tears that welled up in her eyes as reaction set in. When she could no longer hold them back, she let them run down her face, afraid to draw his attention by wiping them away. Finally she had to reach for a handkerchief to blow her nose, but he paid no attention.

As he drew up in front of her house, he broke the silence at last, speaking in a voice devoid of emotion and without turning his head. 'Unless some problem turns up, Gran will be coming home Wednesday morning, and I'll explain then about the engagement. You may tell people whatever story you like about why the engagement has ended, as long as you wait until I've talked to my grandmother. If you don't, I'll see that you regret it.'

Sam shivered, believing him implicitly. 'I would never do anything to hurt your grandmother,' she insisted in a low voice which she fought to keep steady.

He shrugged and finally looked at her. 'I doubt if you will now, at any rate,' he said cynically. His eyes went over her face, but he made no remark about the tear stains which were plainly visible.

'Simon, please let me explain,' she pleaded quietly.

Something seemed to flicker in the hard darkness of his eyes for an instant, but he shook his head and pressed a button on the dashboard. 'Your door is unlocked, Samantha,' he said, with a note of finality in his voice that told her any further attempts to talk to him would be useless.

Turning away from his implacable expression with an aching heart, she got out of the car. The tears started again as she went up the front walk, and she had to fumble around to get her key into the door lock. When she closed the door behind her, she heard Simon drive away.

The rest of Sunday night was unrelieved misery. Sam finally fell asleep exhausted by crying and woke up the next morning deeply depressed. She almost called Richard to say she was sick and wouldn't be in, but in the end keeping busy at work seemed preferable to staying home with her thoughts for company. Fortunately, Mondays were usually busy, and this one was no exception. No one had time to notice that Sam's cheerful smile was at odds with her pale face and the look of pain darkening her eyes.

For once, she did not think that she even wanted to talk to Kate, but when she got home, Kate was out in the garden sketching. A simple enquiry about how her evening with Simon had gone had Sam bursting into tears, and she was ushered firmly into her kitchen, pushed on to a chair, and provided with a box of tissues. By the time she got herself under control again, Kate had everything out for tea, and the kettle was starting to whistle.

'The English left an indelible mark on us,' she commented as Sam mopped up. 'I'm as addicted to coffee as most Americans, but at times like this, I automatically reach for a teapot!'

Sam managed a smile between hiccups. Then, with a cup of tea in hand, she related the whole miserable story, except for the part Kate's suggestion had played. And in spite of not having wanted to talk, she felt better when she was through. A trouble shared might not be halved, she thought, but it did shrink a bit.

'I'd say that Simon is smart enough, and experienced enough, that he ought to have realised you had got out of your depth,' Kate said thoughtfully. 'Unless his blind spot about women has kept him from seeing how inexperienced you are.'

'I didn't give him much reason to see that,' Sam replied with sad honesty. 'I'm still amazed that I actually stopped him last night.'

'A sudden attack of panic can accomplish wonders,' said Kate wryly.

Sam nodded, then shivered in remembrance. 'I've never seen anyone in such a rage!'

'That's because you've never seen a man suffering from terminal frustration before. A whip and a chair can be useful on such occasions. And you don't want to pay much attention to the angry roars; they're usually a lot of "sound and fury, signifying nothing," as Wee Willie Shakespeare once put it.'

'For once I'm afraid "Wee Willie" doesn't apply,' Sam said with an unhappy smile. 'And maybe it's better this way. I can't depend on panic to save me too often. It's just . . . it's just that I'd counted on h-having m-more time with him!'

By Tuesday, however, Sam's depression and tears began to be punctuated by steadily increasing periods of anger, and the memory of herself pleading with him for a chance to explain, started to rankle. Why should she have to explain anything, or justify her actions? It wasn't her fault that he always assumed the worst. Besides, he had been trying to seduce her; if anyone did any justifying, it ought to be Simon. Did he think it was his prerogative to have any woman he wanted?

She had been right about him in the first place: he was a throwback to the times when knights were bold—with any woman unaccompanied by an armed escort. And if he expected her to go into mourning because he had withdrawn his lordly attentions, then he could think again. Sam Abbott wasn't going to make herself miserable over an arrogant anachronism!

If she still ached deep inside and suffered flashes of pain when her glance fell on Simon's ring, at least anger gave her a shield to raise against the grinding sense of loss. And if her eyes were accented by the faintly bruised look of the lids, they were no longer so red-rimmed and puffy from crying.

When she woke up Wednesday morning, Sam lay in bed for a while, wondering what to do with her day off and trying not to remember what she had done last week. What she needed was some hard labour to while away the hours and exhaust herself, she decided, mentally reviewing a list of loathsome tasks which she had been putting off. She finally settled on the kitchen cabinets, which needed to be emptied, scrubbed, and relined with the new shelf paper she had bought three months ago at a sale.

An hour later she was standing in the kitchen armed with a bucket of sudsy water, sponges, shelf paper, ruler, and scissors. Since the wall at the back of the house had the most cabinets, she decided to tackle that first and then work her way around.

By the time she stopped for an early lunch, she had finished the cabinets on the back wall and the end wall, leaving just one set to go. The kitchen smelled faintly of ammonia, even though she had opened the windows and outer door, so she carried her sandwich outside to the back steps. Thank goodness all four walls weren't covered with cabinets, she thought as she sat down with a sigh. Never again would she complain about not having enough space to put things!

She had intended to rest for a while after

eating, but as soon as she relaxed, her thoughts showed a strong inclination to drift in forbidden directions. The flower beds reminded her of the time Simon had come up behind her and startled her; the oak tree reminded her of the day after his party, when the squirrel had driven her away with its scolding. Even the garage reminded her of her car, which in turn recalled the day she had the flat tyre. Giving resting up as a bad job, Sam went back inside.

Soon after she returned to her work, she came to the cabinet over the refrigerator. This cabinet provided a special challenge, since she could only reach it by climbing up on a chair, stepping on to the counter, and leaning over the refrigerator. After numerous trips up and down, she had completed the job, and she was just preparing to descend for the last time when the screen door squeaked open and a familiar voice roared,

'Samantha, what the hell do you think you're doing?'

Sam promptly lost her balance and went backwards off the counter with a cry of alarm. Her fall ended abruptly when her shoulders landed against something hard that grunted, and two arms fastened around her like steel clamps. Her 'Oof!' as the air was squeezed out of her coincided with the double thump of her heels hitting the seat of the chair.

'Damn it, Samantha! Are you trying to kill yourself?'

Sam winced—the roar was almost directly in her ear this time—and dragged her feet off the chair, so that she could stand up. 'I was doing fine until you startled me half to death!' she wheezed. 'Let go of me, you . . . you assassin!'

'And what if something else had startled you when no one was here to catch you?' Simon demanded sternly. He let her go but took hold of her shoulders when she turned. 'From now on, you're going to take better care of yourself, my girl!'

'Oh, yeah?' she retorted inelegantly, her eyes narrowed and smouldering with green fire.

He started to reply, then stopped. His frown began to lift, and he shook his head reprovingly. 'You're supposed to add, "Sez who?"' he reminded her. 'Then I say, "Sez me!" and then you say, "Oh, yeah?" again.'

Sam tried to maintain her anger with the usual lack of success. 'You forgot, "You and who else?"' she said, completing the childhood formula.

'Oh, I intend to handle you all by myself,' he replied, as if she had actually made the retort.

He was smiling when he spoke, but his voice had a caressing note in it that effectively drained the amusement from her face. 'What are you doing here, Simon?' she asked stiffly. If he had decided for some reason to take up again where he had left off, she wanted to set him straight now, before the joy bubbling up inside of her at the sight of him undermined her determination.

He let go of her shoulders and turned partly away from her, brushing back his jacket to shove his hands into his trouser pockets. 'I had a long talk with Gran after I brought her home this morning.'

'She's all right, then?' Sam interrupted.

He nodded, then turned back towards her. 'She already knew all about the engagement. In fact, she knew from the start.'

Sam stared at him blankly, her mind in a whirl. 'But how could she have known?'

'Gran was standing near one of the living-room windows overlooking the terrace when you were talking to that team of gossips you call the Bs. Apparently you were close enough for her to catch every word. She could tell that Mrs What's-her-name had interrupted you and consequently misunderstood what you were saying. And Gran said you looked so appalled that she started to go outside to help you straighten things out. By the time she got there, though, I had just joined the group.'

He paused and then went on, 'The accusations I made to you that night should have been made to Gran. She mistakenly thought that I knew what had really happened, but correctly assumed that I didn't deny we were engaged because of her. She decided to play along, and she even exaggerated her fatigue since the party, so that I would keep up the pretence.'

'But why?' asked Sam, feeling more and more bewildered, though very pleased that her 'crazy' story had now been confirmed.

'She says that she knew I was . . . interested in you, but she was afraid that my disinclination for marriage would stop my interest from developing,' Simon explained. 'So, she thought that I could use a poke in the right direction.'

Sam had a grin. 'That last part sounds like a direct quote!'

'I'm glad you can find it amusing,' he said,

now looking grim. 'I didn't see much humour in it when I remembered some of the things I said to you that night.'

Her grin disappeared as she dropped her eyes and shrugged. 'My story did sound thin. I can understand why you didn't believe me,' she excused awkwardly. Now wasn't the time to tell him how well she understood.

'That's very generous of you, Samantha,' he replied, 'especially after the other night.'

She flushed and looked up again. That sounded as if he might not be blaming her any more for what had happened on Sunday. 'I didn't lead you on deliberately, Simon,' she said earnestly. 'I was just too stupid to realise . . .'

'I'd say "too innocent" is probably more accurate,' he put in as her voice trailed off. 'I never thought that you had a great deal of experience with men, Samantha, but since Sunday I've begun to wonder if you have any real experience at all.' He watched with a slight smile as her lashes dropped to shield her expression, and her face turned fiery red. 'I see that I'm right—and why didn't you tell me, little cat?'

'What was I supposed to do? Say, "Oh, by the way, I'm still a virgin"?' she asked with a spurt of indignation. 'It's not the sort of information you pass out in casual conversation!'

'The other night we were neither conversing, nor casual,' he pointed out. 'You might have saved yourself a good scare if you had told me then.'

'Would you have believed me?' she challenged.

Simon hesitated. 'Maybe not,' he conceded wryly. 'Frustration isn't the best aid to clear, objective thought.' When she made no reply, he added softly, 'Are you going to be generous enough to forgive me for Sunday night, too?'

As Sam saw the new look which appeared in his eyes as he spoke, and as she felt her senses reacting with traitorous promptness to the telltale gleam of gold, the question of exactly what Simon was doing here took on renewed urgency.

'Are you asking me to forgive you for trying to make love to me, or for getting angry when I stopped you?' she asked, while casually stepping back a pace to put a safer distance between them.

Simon moved forward just as casually. 'For getting angry,' he answered without hesitation. 'I still intend to make love to you.'

Sam swallowed and backed up some more. Well, she couldn't complain that he wasn't honest, she thought weakly, searching desperately for a final and convincing way to tell him that he was wasting his time. She cleared her throat to begin, then abruptly changed tack as she felt the edge of the counter at her back and realised that he was still advancing.

'Simon, will you please stand still!'

He grinned. 'We really are going to have to do something about your nerves, little cat! It's not good for you to be so tense.' He rested his hands on the counter on either side of her.

'You're invading my personal space,' she defended. 'That always makes people un-comfortable.'

'Uncomfortable? You're vibrating like a tuning fork, sweetheart,' he scoffed, with such a smugly satisfied smile that Sam lost her temper.

'Don't you laugh at me, you arrogant, conceited, overbearing . . .' she paused to draw

breath, then let it all out again with a whoosh as
he helpfully inserted, '—nasty Baron?'

Then, while she was still speechless, he
continued, 'Just out of curiosity, why "baron" in
particular?'

Sam eyed him balefully and decide he deserved
to know. As she should have expected, though, he
was amused instead of chastened. 'So, you think I
belong in medieval times, do you? Well, dealing
with you would certainly have been simpler then.
I just would have carried you off to my castle the
first time I saw you.'

'But this isn't the Middle Ages,' she said
hastily, alarmed by the way he was looking at her,
'and I am not going to let myself be carried off—
or away. S-so if you're s-still thinking about
s-seducing me, *forget it!*'

Part way through this speech, Simon had bent
his head and started kissing his way up one side
of her throat. At her last words, though, he
paused, and his shoulders shook slightly. 'Are
you absolutely sure?' he murmured as he went
back to nuzzling along her throat.

'Yes!' gasped Sam, leaning more and more
heavily against the counter as her knees started to
give way. She put her hands on his chest to push
him away, but somehow they slipped and ended
up around his neck instead.

'That's a shame,' he whispered huskily as his
lips moved ever closer to her mouth.

'Yes,' she repeated, having lost track of the
conversation, but feeling she ought to contribute
something.

'Gran told me something else, too,' he said,
outlining her lips with kisses.

'Yes?' she breathed.

'She said that you're in love with me.'

'Yes ... *What* did you say?' yelped Sam, jerking her head away.

'Gran told me that you're in love with me,' he repeated obligingly. His voice was calm enough, but had Sam been less appalled by this unexpected shock, she might have noticed that his expression had a guarded intensity, and that his eyes were anxiously watchful.

'Whatever made her say a thing like that?' she asked with a nervous laugh.

He searched her face before replying deliberately, 'She said that if it took me this long to figure out that I'm in love with you—which she could have told me weeks ago—then it would probably take me until Christmas to figure out your feelings, which, I gather, are as plain as the nose on your face to anyone not blind as a bat. And she's getting impatient with all this dilly-dallying around.'

Sam's eyes were wide with sudden hope and doubt. 'Are you?' she whispered.

Simon could feel her trembling, and his arms closed around her as his expression relaxed into an infinitely tender smile. 'I am undoubtedly madly in love with you. And I have certainly been blind as a bat, as well,' he told her, his rough voice softened to a loving caress.

She stared at him for a moment, then laid her head on his shoulder and almost sobbed, 'Oh, Simon! I love you so much, and I've been so miserable!' She was given no chance to say anything more.

By the time coherent conversation was

resumed, Simon was sitting in an armchair in the living-room, and Sam was curled up in his lap. 'Wouldn't the sofa be more comfortable?' she asked as she traced his features with one finger.

'Much too comfortable,' he answered firmly. 'My intentions are now honourable, but my self-control won't stand that kind of strain. In fact, you are very shortly going to have to remove your tempting self to another chair, little cat—especially if you don't sit still and behave!'

'There's no pleasing men,' she sighed. 'You spend weeks trying to get me to misbehave, and then as soon as I do, you change your mind!'

'Hold the thought,' he recommended with a grin. 'In two weeks you may begin misbehaving to your heart's content, and I'll give you all the help and encouragement you could want.'

'Why two weeks?'

'That's when we're getting married, give or take a day or two.'

'Married? . . . Two weeks?'

'We could do it this weekend, except that I plan to carry you off afterwards to some suitably deserted spot, from which we may never return; so I'll need to get things in order at the office,' explained Simon. 'And two weeks will give Richard some time to find at least a temporary replacement for you—not that anyone could ever really replace you, of course.'

'Oh, certainly not,' Sam agreed. The mention of Richard reminded her that she still hadn't told Simon the truth about their relationship, and she decided to clear that out of the way. She was almost certain that he would not overreact but couldn't help feeling a little nervous as she began.

'Er—Simon, speaking of Richard, we weren't really about to get engaged last month,' she said tentatively.

'Of course not, sweetheart. I wouldn't have let you.'

Sam frowned at her beloved. 'You couldn't have . . . Never mind. What I mean is, we just said that for Amanda's benefit.'

Now it was Simon's turn to frown as Sam watched him anxiously. 'Hmm. Richard wanted to hold her at arm's length for a while?' Sam nodded. 'And you were afraid to tell me before.' She nodded again. He picked up her hand and kissed it. 'Thank you for trusting me to understand now, sweetheart,' he told her simply.

'Oh, Simon, I do love you,' she said, giving him a tremulous smile.

'I'm not sure why after the way I've treated you, but I'm not about to question my good fortune,' he replied, then added in a lighter tone, 'and I intend to have you safely married before you have enough time for second thoughts!'

'Like grandfather, like grandson,' Sam teased. 'But aren't you forgetting something?'

'I doubt it,' he said confidently. 'We nasty barons have carrying off damsels down pat. Practice makes perfect, you know.'

'Well, make the most of this carry-off, Baron, because it's going to be your last!' she informed him with a threatening scowl.

Simon laughed. 'I knew you didn't have green eyes for nothing! And I intend to keep much too busy carrying on with you to have time to carry off someone else,' he assured her. 'But what did you think I'd forgotten?'

'You haven't asked me to marry you yet,' she reminded him reprovingly.

'What makes you think you have any choice?' he asked with mock arrogance, then stopped her indignant reply with a quick kiss. 'You'll get your proposal, Samantha, but there's something I want you to know first.' His voice was serious, now, and she waited quietly for him to continue.

'I thought of my feelings for you as a kind of obsession, and after Sunday night I decided that I was going to cure myself of it once and for all,' he began thoughtfully. 'But the more I tried to put you out of my mind, the more impossible I found it to evict you. The thought of not seeing you was so painful that finally I couldn't fool myself any longer. I had to admit that while I'd been concentrating on luring you into my clutches, I'd fallen head over heels into yours.

'As far as I knew, though, all I had going for me were my money and the fact that I attracted you physically. I wanted desperately to see you, but I didn't think you would be willing to listen to an apology, much less a proposal, and I couldn't work up the courage to try.'

'You wanted to ask me to marry you even before your grandmother told you the truth?' Sam interrupted.

'I decided that if you wanted my money, you were welcome to it, as long as you took me as well,' Simon told her with a shrug and a wry smile. 'I knew you weren't indifferent to me, remember, and I was willing to take the risk that you would come to love me.'

Any remaining doubt in Sam's mind disappeared at that confession. If he had been willing to take that kind of chance for her, then he loved her more than she had ever dared to even dream of. She smiled at him, her eyes full of love and wonder.

'I'm glad you told me,' she whispered, her throat tight with tears.

'So, will you marry me, Samantha?' he asked quietly.

'I really *don't* have a choice,' she admitted. 'I love you more than I can say, and of course I'll marry you.'

A tremor ran through him, and his eyes gleamed like burnished gold. 'You won't regret it, my darling. I'll make sure of that!' he vowed as his head bent towards hers. His voice rang with arrogant assurance, but Samantha didn't mind.

Baroness Radnor, she thought as her arms slid around his neck and her lips raised to meet his. Yes, it fitted her very well!

 **ROMANCE**

Next month's romances from Mills & Boon

Each month, you can choose from a world of variety in romance with Mills & Boon. These are the new titles to look out for next month.

AN ELUSIVE MISTRESS Lindsay Armstrong
ABODE OF PRINCES Jayne Bauling
POPPY GIRL Jacqueline Gilbert
TO SPEAK OF LOVE Claudia Jameson
A MAN POSSESSED Penny Jordan
VILLA IN THE SUN Marjorie Lewty
LAND OF THUNDER Annabel Murray
THE LAST BARRIER Edwina Shore
ONE LIFE AT A TIME Natalie Spark
SO NEAR, SO FAR Jessica Steele
*AT DAGGERS DRAWN Margaret Mayo
*BOSS OF YARRAKINA Valerie Parv

Buy them from your usual paperback stockist, or write to: Mills & Boon Reader Service, P.O. Box 236, Thornton Rd, Croydon, Surrey CR9 3RU, England. Readers in South Africa - write to: Mills & Boon Reader Service of Southern Africa, Private Bag X3010, Randburg, 2125.

*These two titles are available *only* from Mills & Boon Reader Service.

Mills & Boon
the rose of romance

Mills & Boon

Take 4 Exciting Books Absolutely FREE

Love, romance, intrigue... all are captured for you by Mills & Boon's top-selling authors. By becoming a regular reader of Mills & Boon's Romances you can enjoy 6 superb new titles every month plus a whole range of special benefits: your very own personal membership card, a free monthly newsletter packed with recipes, competitions, exclusive book offers and a monthly guide to the stars, plus extra bargain offers and big cash savings.

**AND an Introductory FREE GIFT for YOU.
Turn over the page for details.**

As a special introduction we will send you four exciting Mills & Boon Romances Free and without obligation when you complete and return this coupon.

At the same time we will reserve a subscription to Mills & Boon Reader Service for you. Every month, you will receive 6 of the very latest novels by leading Romantic Fiction authors, delivered direct to your door. You don't pay extra for delivery — postage and packing is always completely Free. There is no obligation or commitment — you can cancel your subscription at any time.

You have nothing to lose and a whole world of romance to gain.

Just fill in and post the coupon today to MILLS & BOON READER SERVICE, FREEPOST, P.O. BOX 236, CROYDON, SURREY CR9 9EL.

Please Note:- READERS IN SOUTH AFRICA write to Independent Book Services P.T.Y., Postbag X3010, Randburg 2125, S. Africa

---

FREE BOOKS CERTIFICATE

To: Mills & Boon Reader Service, FREEPOST, P.O. Box 236, Croydon, Surrey CR9 9EL.

Please send me, free and without obligation, four Mills & Boon Romances, and reserve a Reader Service Subscription for me. If I decide to subscribe I shall, from the beginning of the month following my free parcel of books, receive six new books each month for £6.60, post and packing free. If I decide not to subscribe, I shall write to you within 10 days The free books are mine to keep in any case. I understand that I may cancel my subscription at any time simply by writing to you. I am over 18 years of age.

Please write in BLOCK CAPITALS.

Signature _____

Name _____

Address _____

_____ Post code _____

SEND NO MONEY — TAKE NO RISKS.

Please don't forget to include your Postcode.

Remember, postcodes speed delivery. Offer applies in UK only and is not valid to present subscribers. Mills & Boon reserve the right to exercise discretion in granting membership. If price changes are necessary you will be notified.

6R   Offer expires July 31st 1986.

EP86